Relapse Prevention Counseling

*Clinical Strategies to Guide
Addiction Recovery and Reduce Relapse*

Tools for Individual
or Group Setting

Treatment Models
& Therapies

Group Sessions
for Substance Use &
Co-Occurring Disorders

Dennis C. Daley, PhD & Antoine Douaihy, MD

"Drs. Daley and Douaihy offer individual and group practitioners an array of tools and strategies for practice, relapse prevention and recovery management that will make treatment more relevant and outcomes more successful. They add unique and exceptional insights for addressing the dually diagnosed, for strengthening relapse prevention and for including the critical role of the family in treatment. This work documents the evolution of our field. All professionals and agencies need to know it … and follow it."

-**Michael T. Flaherty, PhD**
Clinical Psychologist Founder – Institute for Research,
Education and Treatment of Addiction, Pittsburgh

Published by
PESI Publishing & Media
PESI, Inc
3839 White Ave
Eau Claire, WI 54703

Cover: Amy Rubenzer
Editing: Marietta Whittlesey
Layout: Bookmasters & Amy Rubenzer

ISBN: 9781937661687

Printed in the United States of America.

Library of Congress Cataloging-in-Publication Data

Daley, Dennis C.
  Relapse prevention counseling : strategies to promote recovery and reduce relapse risk from substance use and co-occurring disorders / Dennis C. Daley, Ph.D., Antoine Douaihy, M.D.
    pages cm
  Includes bibliographical references and index.
  ISBN 978-1-937661-68-7 (alk. paper)
  1. Substance abuse--Relapse--Prevention. 2. Compulsive behavior--Relapse--Prevention. 3. Substance abuse--Treatment. 4. Compulsive behavior--Treatment. I. Douaihy, Antoine B., 1965- II. Title.
  RC564.D346 2015
  362.29'17--dc23
                                                    2015024459

PESI
Publishing
& Media
www.pesipublishing.com

Authors' Note

We would like to thank Janis McDonald for her help updating this book. Janis spent considerable time with multiple rewrites, editing, and organizing references.

Comments about this book or information about clinical workshops on Relapse Prevention can be sent to the first author at daleypublications@yahoo.com.

Table of Contents

Dedication to G. Alan Marlatt

We dedicate this book to the memory of a friend and colleague, Alan Marlatt. He was a Professor of Psychology and the Director of the Addictive Behaviors Research Center at the University of Washington in Seattle. Alan was a pioneer in the field of substance use disorders (SUDs) and the first to publish a comprehensive review of relapse prevention (RP) and focus on the importance of helping clients learn skills to manage their SUDs, change their lives and take action early if they were unable to stay sober. His influence on the fields of SUDs and psychology was enormous. Alan stimulated the SUDs treatment field with his forward thinking, his research and his teaching on numerous topics related to SUDs, treatment, recovery and relapse.

He was a good friend and mentor to many of us in the U.S. and other countries. Alan was well respected for his many contributions to the field, and his book on RP is one of the most highly referenced books in the literature. His work led to an increased focus on RP in the field of mental health treatment.

I (DD) first learned about Alan's work in the 1980s when I worked as a therapist in a residential treatment program and read a book chapter he wrote on relapse in SUDs. His framework for understanding the multiple causes of relapse and intervention strategies was impressive. In a time before the age of the internet, I called him to discuss his ideas and what I was doing in the area of RP in a treatment program. He was receptive to my call, very helpful and respectful and interested in my clinical work. This led to a long-term relationship. I brought Alan to Pittsburgh on numerous occasions to present on RP. We co-presented at several conferences in the U.S. together. We invited each other to co-author articles and books. And, we talked by phone or email throughout the years to keep up on what each other was doing. In the early years I referred to him as the "grandfather of RP."

Many newspapers (such as *The NY Times*) and magazine articles (such as *Time*) have been written about Dr. Marlatt to share appreciation for his impact on individuals and his field. His good friend and colleague, Dennis Donovan, PhD from the University of Washington (also a friend and colleague of ours) stated that, "Alan has been a mentor, friend, and colleague to many of us here at UW, and his network of associates and those whom he has touched personally and professionally is extensive and international in scope. We have lost a true visionary and luminary in the field of SUDs. He will leave his prints in our hearts and minds, and there is a cadre of us to carry on the important work that he has championed throughout his career." Another colleague, Dr. Fred Rogers, the President of the Society on SUDs Psychology said, "It is impossible to recount briefly how much Alan has meant to the field of SUDs psychology, to SUDs treatment and research. Alan also had a direct impact on many of us through his friendship, mentorship and genuine humanity."

About the Authors

DENNIS C. DALEY, PhD

Dr. Daley is professor of psychiatry in the department of psychiatry at Western Psychiatric Institute and Clinic (WPIC) at the University of Pittsburgh School of Medicine. He served for 14 years as chief of addiction medicine services (AMS) at WPIC. AMS includes a large continuum of prevention, intervention and treatment programs in multiple settings. He has provided clinical care to clients and families for over 35 years. Dr. Daley also holds an appointment as professor of social work at the University of Pittsburgh and served for 10 years as a part-time faculty member at The Pennsylvania State University and 10 years at Indiana University of Pennsylvania. Dr. Daley has presented hundreds of educational and training programs throughout the U.S. and Canada, and in Mexico, Europe and Asia.

Dr. Daley is principal investigator of the Appalachian Tri-State (ATS) Node of the Clinical Trials Network (CTN) of The National Institute on Drug Abuse (NIDA). He has served as researcher on numerous studies funded by NIDA, the National Institute on Alcohol Abuse and Alcoholism, and other sources. Dr. Daley has been a trainer or consultant on studies at Harvard Medical School, the University of Pittsburgh School of Medicine and Spaulding University.

Dr. Daley has over 300 publications including books and workbooks on recovery from addiction, mental illness, co-occurring disorders, relapse prevention, emotions, moods, and family recovery. He has written materials for children and adolescents as well as adults. Dr. Daley developed and wrote 35 educational videos including the highly popular *Living Sober* interactive series, and *Staying Sober, Keeping Straight*, an educational program on relapse prevention for individuals in treatment. Several of his books and recovery guides have been translated to foreign languages. He was one of the first in the U.S. to develop clinical programs, a treatment manual, and recovery materials on relapse prevention for individuals in recovery and collaborated with the late Dr. G. Alan Marlatt who is considered the pioneer of relapse prevention. Dr. Daley also contributes regular columns to *The Counselor* on issues in behavioral healthcare, and to *Counselor Connection* on recovery and personal growth.

He has consulted with numerous treatment programs and facilities in the U.S. and Europe, including an employee assistance program, athletic department, health plan and the veterans administration healthcare system.

ANTOINE DOUAIHY, MD

Dr. Douaihy is associate professor of psychiatry, medical director of Addiction Medicine Services and medical director of WPIC's inpatient dual diagnosis programs. He also serves as the senior psychiatrist at the Pittsburgh AIDS Center for Treatment of the University of Pittsburgh Medical Center (UPMC). Dr. Douaihy has provided clinical leadership and services for many years throughout UPMC and at the School of Medicine. He has expertise in helping individuals with substance use, psychiatric or co-occurring disorders, including those with HIV or Hepatitis C. Dr. Douaihy also has a strong interest in medication-assisted treatments for addiction, including smoking cessation treatments for tobacco use disorders

Dr. Douaihy has worked with Dr. Daley on several clinical, educational and research projects, and served as the principal investigator on five studies. He is medical director and an investigator in the ATS Node of the Clinical Trials Network project. Dr. Douaihy has organized and presented numerous workshops, symposia, and Grand Rounds, nationally and internationally on numerous clinical topics. Dr. Douaihy has been or is an investigator on numerous NIDA, NIAAA, NIMH or industry-sponsored trials, including psychosocial interventions and motivational interviewing. He collaborates as a Co-I on projects with the Pennsylvania Mid-Atlantic AIDS Education and Training Center (AETC) and serves as a member of the Pittsburgh HIV Commission. Over the past 15 years, Dr. Douaihy has received 20 awards for outstanding teaching of medical students and psychiatric residents and has been a champion in promoting the need for physicians to integrate focus on substance use problems among individuals treated in medical and psychiatric settings. He has authored or co-authored numerous books and chapters, papers, and recovery guides for individuals and families.

Introduction and Overview

PURPOSE OF BOOK

The purpose of this book is to help clinicians and other providers understand and facilitate the process of recovery and reduce the risk of relapse among clients or patients with substance use disorders, including those with co-occurring psychiatric disorders. We conducted a training needs survey of a large group of clinicians who provide treatment in numerous residential and ambulatory addiction medicine and psychiatric programs. A major area of clinical interest was relapse prevention (RP). We learned that clinicians do not read a lot, perhaps because they are busy with work and personal lives. Therefore, this book is for busy clinicians who have limited time to read.

Our primary goal is to provide clinical strategies and tools to use in individual, group or family sessions. Sources of information for this book are clinical trials, meta-analyses of treatment studies, clinical literature, treatment manuals, recovery literature, our extensive experiences as clinicians, researchers and educators, and our experiences developing clinical programs and materials for individuals and families that focus on recovery and RP.

Chapter 1 provides an overview of recovery, definitions of lapse and relapse for SUDs, and relapse and recurrence for psychiatric disorders. Determinants and effects of lapse, relapse and recurrence are then discussed.

Chapter 2 provides an overview of relapse prevention (RP), treatment models that incorporate RP principles, specific models of RP and research support for RP. Readers can consult the references at the end of this book for more information on a specific approach.

Chapter 3 discusses counseling strategies to promote recovery and reduce relapse risk. These are organized in the following categories:

- Motivation for change
- Adherence and retention in treatment and recovery programs
- Managing a substance use and/or other addictive disorder
- Managing a psychiatric illness
- Medication-assisted treatments
- Managing emotions
- Family and interpersonal relationships

- Support systems and mutual support programs
- Relapse prevention and intervention
- Lifestyle changes

The term "skills" is used throughout as clients need to learn coping strategies, or skills, to manage their disorder(s) and engage in a recovery process.

Chapter 4 discusses counseling tools that can be used in individual, group or family sessions. They can be used in any type of addiction treatment program (detoxification, residential, ambulatory, opioid maintenance or other specialty programs), or mental health program that focuses on co-occurring disorders (CODs).

Chapter 5 reviews group interventions and formats for outpatient and residential settings, orienting clients to groups, and strategies for group leaders to cover specific content in group sessions. It gives details on creating RP groups (topics, objectives, points to cover, and methods to cover the topics). This chapter also provides 12 structured RP group topics that can make up a "core" RP program for clients.

Chapter 6 includes structured groups on RP with co-occurring disorders. These groups are structured similarly to those in Chapter 7.

Chapter 7 reviews process therapy or problem solving groups that focus on a broad range of issues in ongoing recovery and RP for clients with SUDs or co-occurring disorders. This chapter covers the purposes of these groups, objectives and format. It also addresses the problems commonly discussed in these groups as well as problems encountered in the group process.

Chapter 8 discusses relapse and the family. It reviews goals and formats of family groups and provides family education groups that can be used in hospital, residential or ambulatory settings. This chapter also discusses mutual support programs for families and family recovery.

An appendix provides references cited and a list of websites where the reader can access additional information on recovery and RP.

CHAPTER 1

Recovery and Relapse Prevention

Substance use disorders (SUDs) represent a significant problem for affected individuals, families and society. These disorders cost the United States hundreds of billions of dollars a year as a result of crime, and costs related to work loss, and healthcare and social services (medical or psychiatric care, criminal justice, child welfare, public assistance). SUDs are associated with lower lifespan as a result of accidents, suicides and medical diseases caused or worsened by a SUD. In addition, these disorders often have a heavy psychological, emotional, economic and spiritual impact on affected individuals and their families. The average North American has about a 15% chance of developing a SUD in the course of their lifetime, and at any given time the prevalence rate is about 8% of the adult population. In 2012, 22.2 million Americans ages 12 and older had a SUD in the past year. Of those, 2.8 million had problems with both alcohol and drugs, 4.5 million had problems with drugs only, and 14.9 million had problems with alcohol only. Several major epidemiologic studies show high rates of psychiatric illness among individuals with SUDs, which can complicate recovery and impact on relapse to the SUD after a period of recovery.

For many people, SUDs are chronic conditions in which relapse is common. According to McLellan and colleagues, rates of relapse with SUDs are similar to those of other chronic medical conditions. While these rates vary across studies, about 40–60% of those receiving treatment will relapse at least once, and many will relapse multiple times. Preventing relapse or reducing its extent is therefore a prerequisite for any attempt to facilitate successful, long-term changes in substance use behaviors. Relapse prevention (RP) was a phrase coined in the late 1970s by Dr. Alan Marlatt to describe a theoretical model and to provide an umbrella term for a set of cognitive-behavioral intervention strategies designed to reduce the likelihood and severity of relapse following the cessation or reduction of substance use. Also, relapses vary in severity and a majority of individuals receiving treatment stop or reduce substance use, and show improvements in functioning and quality of life. Hence, treatment has many positive outcomes even if total abstinence from alcohol or other drugs is not sustained.

RECOVERY FROM SUBSTANCE USE DISORDERS

Daley and Marlatt describe recovery as a long-term process of change through which an individual achieves abstinence and improves health, wellness and quality of life. While some clients establish and maintain long periods of continuous sobriety, many have periods of remission followed by episodes of relapse. Due to the relapsing nature of SUDs, many clients may need multiple episodes of treatment over time, similar to other chronic medical or psychiatric disorders. Therefore, many clients need to return to treatment to stabilize from

1

periods of relapse. One of the principles of treatment delineated by the National Institute on Drug Abuse is that, *"Remaining in treatment for an adequate period of time is critical,"* and *"that recovery is a long-term process that frequently requires multiple episodes of treatment."*

Recovery may encompass any area of the addicted person's functioning. While abstinence from drugs and alcohol is the main goal of treatment, personal and lifestyle changes are viewed as needed to improve the chances of abstinence, reduce the risk of relapse and enhance the quality of life.

Recovery as a process may occur in three phases according to Dr. G. Alan Marlatt, who has written extensively about SUDs and RP.

1. ***The first phase involves making a commitment to change.*** The client makes an agreement to participate in treatment even if abstinence is not the accepted goal at first. As long as the client acknowledges there is some problem associated with substance use, some commitment can be made. In treatment, clients with weak commitment to recovery will have the opportunity to reassess their situations and develop motivation to change.

2. ***The second phase involves stopping drug and alcohol use.*** While some clients achieve this change relatively easily, most struggle with it and experience multiple lapses and relapses over time. Many do not achieve ongoing abstinence during their first attempt at change. This is not a sign of failure. It implies that a SUD is a chronic relapsing illness.

3. ***The third phase of recovery is maintenance or relapse prevention.*** This refers to maintaining behavior change over time after it is initiated. Relapse prevention (RP) refers to coping strategies to help clients identify and manage warning signs of relapse and high-risk relapse factors following a period of successful sobriety. RP strategies aim to help clients integrate changes into their daily lives after formal treatment has ended.

Recovery is best viewed as a nonlinear process. Many clients go through ups and downs during their recovery. Some take many steps forward than a step backwards. Struggling or having a relapse is not a sign that the treatment has failed or the client has failed as long as clients learn from their experiences.

Recovery is a process that involves making a commitment to sobriety and changing oneself and one's lifestyle. Recovery is overcoming the problems associated with SUDs and developing a balanced and healthy lifestyle in which drugs and alcohol have no place.

Recovery is both learning skills to *abstain from alcohol or other mood altering drugs* (except in cases requiring medication for a medical or psychiatric problem) and *changing oneself and one's lifestyle* to support this abstinence. Someone making positive personal or lifestyle changes is more likely to abstain from using substances; the person who abstains from substances is more likely to make positive personal or lifestyle changes.

RECOVERY FROM PSYCHIATRIC OR CO-OCCURRING DISORDERS

SAMHSA defines recovery as a "process of change through which individuals improve their health and wellness, live a self-directed life and strive to reach their full potential." This means managing the psychiatric illness and the SUD by addressing the major domains of life (physical, psychological, social, interpersonal, spiritual) to determine changes to make. Recovery is based on the need to accept the disorders, manage acute and persistent symptoms of psychiatric illness since some symptoms of chronic disorders will not remit totally, accept help and support from others and address problems contributing to or resulting from the disorders. The following strategies can aid recovery from a co-occurring psychiatric disorder:

- Becoming educated about the disorder(s) (signs, symptoms, causes, effects, treatment, recovery, relapse).
- Developing a desire to change and improve oneself. Motivation for recovery can change, especially in the early phases. As with SUDs, recovery from a COD is not linear. While a client can have stronger motivation to manage the SUD or the psychiatric disorder, long-term stable recovery requires managing both types of disorders.
- Setting goals to change. These can relate to the two types of disorders, work, school, family, interpersonal relationships, use of leisure time, living situation or managing financial resources.
- Following the change plan and complying with counseling appointments or taking medicine as prescribed.
- Following a routine and building structure into daily life to have a sense of purpose, and meaningful activities and relationships.
- Involving the family or concerned significant other.
- Getting active in mutual support programs.
- Seeking help or support from other people or organizations.
- Avoiding alcohol or drug use and high-risk people when possible.
- Focusing on positive emotions and people.

FACTORS AFFECTING RECOVERY

Recovery is a *long-term process*. The areas of change during recovery may relate to physical, psychological, social, family, or spiritual functioning. Since each person has a different profile of strengths and weaknesses in these areas, each person requires a unique *recovery program* based on these factors:

Severity: How long has the SUD been a problem? What are the patterns of use, amounts, frequency, consequences and methods of use (oral ingestion, snorting, or injecting drugs with a needle or sharing needles or other equipment with other users)?

Demographics: The age, sex, and ethnicity of the person. There are many subgroups that may have special recovery needs, for example: women, adolescents, older people, African Americans, Native Americans, and LGBT individuals.

Magnitude of damage: Serious medical, psychiatric, family or legal problems may require different treatment services and recovery strategies than those less damaged.

Perception of problem: If the client sees the SUDs as an "illness" or "disease," as opposed to a matter of "willpower," it is more likely that professional treatment will be accepted and a program of recovery will be followed.

Motivation: This may be external, such as to save a job or marriage, avoid going to jail, or avoid paying a fine. It can be internal, such as a person seeking help for himself. At first, the person does not need internal motivation to benefit from treatment or involvement in a recovery program. There are benefits from treatment even if the client is "forced" or "pressured" into it. Eventually, motivation must become internalized if sobriety and personal change are to continue over the long-term.

Social support: How adequate and intact is the client's family and social support system? Does she have others upon whom she can rely for help and support with problems? Does she have a confidant with whom she can share thoughts, feelings or problems?

Resources: What treatment or recovery resources are available to the addicted person? Is there money to pay for professional care? During the past decade, managed care has had a significant impact on the amount of professional treatment services authorized and paid for. For example, years ago a residential rehabilitation program generally lasted at least four full weeks. Insurance companies didn't have to "pre-authorize" or pre-approve care. Today, insurance companies cover many of these programs for less than 14 days and they must first be pre-approved by the client's insurance company.

Giving up alcohol or drugs can be painful and difficult. Recovery often requires physiological and psychological adaptations that are stressful or uncomfortable at first. Many individuals are unsure if they want to, or even can, give up the substance they are dependent on. They struggle with accepting their problem or the need for help from others.

Recovery requires *acceptance* of the SUD and a *plan or program of recovery*, which usually includes professional treatment and/or mutual support programs such as AA, NA, CA, CMA, Women for Sobriety (WFS), SMART Recovery, Rational Recovery, or other mutual support programs.

There are no "quick fixes" or '"easy cures" for SUDs. Recovery takes time, hard work, and often requires help and support from professionals, other recovering people, family, or friends.

LAPSE AND RELAPSE FOR SUBSTANCE USE DISORDERS

Since many substance use disorders are chronic, relapse is common as it is with other medical diseases or psychiatric disorders, especially those chronic in nature. Most SUD relapses occur within the first year of treatment. And within this first year, most relapses occur within the first 90 days. Dropout rates are usually the highest in the first month of treatment. Clients who drop out of treatment are at increased risk for relapse.

Lapse refers to the initial episode of substance use following a period of recovery. A lapse may or may not end up in a relapse. This depends on how the client thinks about and responds to an initial lapse.

Relapse is defined from two perspectives: 1) relapse is the *actual event* of substance use; or 2) relapse is the *process* of falling back to unhealthy habits or attitudes that often lead to substance use following a period of abstinence. Warning signs occur before the actual use of substances.

The client in a relapse process usually shows signs of changes in attitudes, thoughts, emotions or behaviors. At this early stage, the clinician can sometimes intervene to help the client prevent a return to substance use. However, this depends on the client's ability to recognize these signs and take action. Recognizing emotional and behavioral signs of relapse are sometimes difficult, however. These signs are often subtle. Then too, different people show different warning signs. A relapse warning sign for one client may be irrelevant for another. Also, since behavior may be unconsciously motivated, the client may actually be unaware of warning signs that are apparent to other people.

RELAPSE AND RECURRENCE FOR PSYCHIATRIC DISORDERS

Relapse for a psychiatric disorder refers to a return or worsening of symptoms during the acute phase of treatment. For example, a client with clinical depression may be doing well with most symptoms improved or remitted, then experience a return of some symptoms of depressive illness during the current episode of treatment. A recurrence refers to a new episode of illness after a period of sustained recovery. Clients vary in terms of how much time elapses between episodes of illness. For example, one client with clinical depression may not experience a recurrent episode for over a year, whereas another client may be depression free for several years before experiencing a recurrent episode.

DETERMINANTS OF LAPSE, RELAPSE OR RECURRENCE

There is no simple explanation of why a person relapses following a period of recovery. Relapse can defy logic, leaving you puzzled about why someone returns to substance use after doing well, especially after long periods of recovery. Even individuals with stable recovery from a psychiatric illness can show signs of relapse or recurrence during periods in which life is going well.

Many causes of relapse and recurrence have been identified from research, the experiences of recovering individuals, their families and from the work of professionals. Knowledge of relapse precipitants can be used to educate clients and their families, and help them identify their personal high-risk relapse factors as well as strategies to manage these.

According to researchers and clinicians, relapse is caused by an interaction of many variables: affective, behavioral, cognitive, environment, relationships, physiological, psychological, spiritual, and treatment-related. Although these variables are separated for discussion, they are often interrelated.

Affective (feelings/emotions, moods): The more common emotional states contributing to relapse are anger, anxiety, boredom, depression, and loneliness. In a small number of cases, positive emotional states affect relapse. Many individuals with anxiety disorders have symptoms of depression, and many with clinical depression have symptoms of anxiety. In either instance, one type of symptom can impact on managing the other type of affective symptom. For SUDs, however, *it is not the emotional state that determines if a relapse will occur, but the client's ability to use active coping skills to manage this emotion*.

Behavioral: Clients are more prone to relapse if they have poor problem solving, social, stress management and leisure time management skills. The greater the repertoire of cognitive and behavioral coping skills, the more likely the person is to manage the challenges of recovery and maintain abstinence. Many of the illness management approaches used with psychiatric or co-occurring disorders aim to help clients increase skills in these areas, which enhance their recovery.

Cognitive: The client's attitudes or beliefs towards substance use, a SUD, a psychiatric disorder, or recovery, beliefs about the ability to cope with difficult situations and expectancies for one's behaviors can contribute to relapse. For example, if a client believes that she can successfully cope with a difficult challenge, such as a drug craving or pressure from friends to use drugs, relapse is less of a threat to recovery. On the other hand, if a client believes recovery is intolerable, not fun or a chore, relapse is more likely.

Environment and relationships: The availability of substances, social pressures to engage in substance use and major unexpected life changes for which the client is ill prepared. Poor social support systems or networks made up primarily of others who abuse substances or have SUDs themselves, are potentially dangerous to the recovering person. So is a non-supportive, hostile family, or one resistant to becoming involved in recovery when such involvement is critical. This is not to say that others should be blamed for a person's relapse, but to acknowledge that other people and conditions in the social environment affect both recovery and relapse. Family involvement in treatment of psychiatric illness has a positive impact in clinical outcome, and reduces the risk of relapse and re-hospitalization.

Physiological: These variables include cravings for substances, brain chemistry, diet, physical illness or pain and poor rest and relaxation practices. Medications such as narcotics used to treat pain, benzodiazepines to treat anxiety disorders, stimulants to treat attention deficit or other disorders, and other medications used to treat dental or medical problems can contribute to a client's desire to use substances and eventually relapse. Chronic pain that is not managed sufficiently can contribute to relapse to anxiety, depression or substance use. Studies of brain imaging indicate that it can take a long time to recover from substances of abuse, but recovery is possible.

Psychological: Motivation, learned behaviors, personality factors and psychological disturbances stemming from traumas can contribute to a relapse. Clients with CODs are at higher risk for relapse if their psychiatric disorders are not treated. Research shows that childhood trauma compromises neural structure and function, making an individual susceptible to later cognitive deficits and psychiatric illnesses, including schizophrenia, major depression, bipolar disorder, post-traumatic stress disorder (PTSD), and SUDs. Particularly, the link between trauma exposure and substance abuse has been well-established. In the National Survey of Adolescents, teens who had experienced physical or sexual abuse/assault were three times more likely to report past or current substance abuse than those without a history of trauma. In surveys of adolescents receiving treatment for substance abuse, more than 70% of patients had a history of trauma exposure.

Spiritual: Guilt and shame, and lack of meaning or purpose in life may contribute to relapse. Some clients feel an "emptiness" or "void" when they stop using substances. If this is not filled with meaningful activities or relationships, the risk of relapse is greater. The same holds true with recovery from psychiatric disorders. Clients need meaning in their lives in order to feel good and manage their psychiatric disorders.

Treatment and recovery related: A practitioner can directly and indirectly contribute to a client's relapse through expressing negative attitudes, negative feelings or by showing enabling behaviors. Treatment agencies can influence relapse by delaying necessary services with long waiting lists. An example would be a client who completes a residential rehabilitation program and then is placed on a 3-week waiting list for outpatient services. Or, a client discharged from a psychiatric hospital who needs a follow-up visit with a psychiatrist to manage medications, but who is not scheduled for weeks or months after discharge. Even sponsors or other recovering people can do or say things that can contribute to a person's relapse. For example, an alcoholic struggling with strong desires to drink was overwhelmed with mixed feelings about staying sober. When she discussed these with a recovering friend, the friend said, "you aren't ready to quit, you haven't hit bottom yet." She was given the message that she was expected to act out her conflicts and go on a binge. Perhaps then she would finally discover that she could not safely drink.

The important point is that many factors can directly or indirectly contribute to relapse. The best way for relapse to be understood is to consider these different variables.

There are some clients who will not care much about recovery or have low motivation to change. While the clinician should not give up on unmotivated clients, we all have our limitations. Such poor motivation can stem from the SUDs, a psychiatric disorder or other psychological problem. However, keep in mind that many people with poor motivation eventually become motivated and recover from their disorders. Often, this is influenced by clinicians who use motivational interventions and express patience, empathy and compassion.

EFFECTS OF LAPSE, RELAPSE OR RECURRENCE

Relapse effects differ, depending both on the client and his life situation. Factors influencing the outcomes or effects of relapse are the amount, types, and length of the substance use episode, physical and mental health of the person relapsing, behaviors, beliefs about SUDs, recovery and relapse, prior treatment and relapse history and the person's ability to use relapse interruption plans to limit how long a relapse lasts.

There are different "types" of relapses. One type is "the therapeutic" relapse, which helps a person's recovery. For example, Jim, a heroin addict and alcoholic, lazily worked his recovery program and smoked marijuana. Jim argued that he could control marijuana use and not go back to heroin, which was his primary drug of choice. He firmly believed his "days of shooting dope were over" because of how it wrecked his life. But within a month of smoking marijuana, Jim was shooting dope again. He learned through this relapse that his goal of controlled substance use was hopeless and that "his" recovery plan was not working. From his relapse, he finally accepted the recommendation of his clinician and became involved in regular counseling and the NA program. He adopted a program of total abstinence.

On the other extreme is the "fatal" relapse that tragically ends in death. Louis, a heroin addict, died during his last relapse as a result of a drug overdose. Megan, an alcoholic, died in a car accident after relapsing to alcohol and driving while intoxicated.

Between these extremes are many variations of negative consequences, from mild to very severe. Clinicians should evaluate each relapse individually to determine the actual effects on the addicted person's life and the lives of those close to him. Sometimes, adverse effects of a relapse can help motivate the client to work harder at recovery or improve the recovery plan.

Many psychiatric and SUDs are chronic, relapsing illnesses, characterized by a cycle of patterns of symptom manifestation, treatment, improvement, relapse or recurrence of symptoms and a return to treatment if the client drops out early. Thus, effective treatment of either or both conditions requires close monitoring and needs to be long-term for maintenance of gains and early intervention when a relapse or recurrence occurs.

Among those who receive substance abuse treatment, the presence of any psychiatric disorder will likely contribute to a persistent threat of relapse to substance use. While not everyone will relapse, the risk of relapse for those with co-occurring disorders demands a system of treatment and service delivery support that is extended to enhance continuity of care, sustain recovery, wherein adherence to medication regimens, behavioral change, and early signs of relapse are closely monitored.

CHAPTER 2

Relapse Prevention Therapies

TREATMENT MODELS INCORPORATING RP PRINCIPLES

The principles and concepts of relapse prevention (RP, also called relapse prevention therapy or RPT) are used with other addictive disorders, impulse control disorders, marital problems, psychiatric illness and co-occurring psychiatric disorders. RP is designed to help the individual with any of these disorders or problems focus on reducing the likelihood of a recurrence of the behavior or symptoms of the disorder. The "maintenance" phase of treatment is important in helping clients maintain their gains.

The goals of SUDs treatment are to help the client initiate abstinence, improve functioning and prevent or reduce the risk of relapse. RP for SUDs generally refers to three types of clinical interventions: 1) a specific program or intervention that focuses primarily on relapse issues and the maintenance stage of treatment; 2) any individual or group psychosocial treatment that aims to help clients reduce or stop substance use, prepare for recovery and cope with high-risk relapse factors, and reduce the likelihood of relapse; and 3) medication-assisted treatment that helps clients with more severe forms of SUDs. Evidenced-based interventions include:

- Cognitive-Behavioral or Coping Skills Therapies
- Community Reinforcement Approach
- Contingency Management (Motivational Incentives)
- Motivational Interviewing
- Marital and Family Therapies
- Group Counseling
- Individual Drug Counseling
- MATRIX Model for Stimulant SUDs
- Recovery Management Checkups
- Relapse Prevention (also called Relapse Prevention Therapy)
- Twelve-Step Facilitation Therapy
- Medication-Assisted Treatments (for alcohol, opioid or nicotine dependence)

Clinicians can incorporate RP into their individual, group or family work. Exposing clients to the major issues and principles of RP can aid their ongoing recovery and reduce relapses. Many of the clinical models listed above focus on RP as one area of focus during the treatment. For example, the cognitive behavioral coping skills therapy approach developed by Kadden, Monti and colleagues, used in the NIAAA sponsored Project MATCH study, helps clients develop coping skills to manage cravings and thoughts of drinking alcohol, refuse offers to drink, cope with a lapse to prevent it from leading to a full-blown relapse, and understand how 'seemingly-irrelevant-decisions' can impact on relapse. The twelve-step facilitation therapy model developed by Nowinski and Baker used in Project MATCH reduce relapse risk by helping clients understand and actively use the tools of the AA program.

The individual drug counseling (IDC) model developed by Mercer and Woody, and the group drug counseling (GDC) model developed by Daley, Mercer and Carpenter for a NIDA sponsored large-scale, multi-site clinical trial of cocaine dependent individuals placed considerable attention on issues of relapse and RP. Both IDC and GDC provided specific sessions on RP issues as well as the opportunity for clients to discuss close calls, lapses, relapses and strategies to re-establish abstinence if substances were used.

RP has also been added to behavioral marital therapy (BMT). This BMT approach focuses both on relationship issues within the marriage as well as issues affecting relapse.

The MATRIX model of structured outpatient treatment developed by Rawson and colleagues in the treatment of cocaine or methamphetamine dependence includes considerable focus on RP in both individual and group sessions. This program offers stabilization, education, RP, family, and therapy groups. Topic-oriented RP groups are a central component of this model. The general goal of RP is to help addicted clients understand relapse and learn strategies to reduce the likelihood of a relapse occurring. Each RP group session involves the presentation of material relevant to relapse followed by a discussion of this material. Clients then have the opportunity to discuss recent problems or issues, which could impact on relapse. Sessions use informational and interactive handouts as well to help clients personalize the information. There are 19 topics in the RP module, which address issues such as relapse warning signs, relapse justification, lifestyle balance, and keeping a distance from relapse.

COMMON ELEMENTS OF RP

Most RP models incorporate principles or clinical strategies from Marlatt's original conceptualization of relapse. Despite any differences in theoretical underpinnings, philosophy of treatment or intervention strategies, models of RP have several components in common. They focus on the need for clients with a SUD to:

- Have a broad repertoire of cognitive and behavioral coping strategies to draw upon for identifying and managing high-risk situations and warning signs of relapse.
- Make lifestyle changes to decrease the need for addictive substances.
- Increase healthy activities and pleasures.
- Prepare for interrupting lapses to minimize damage and prevent these from becoming full-blown relapses; and learn to intervene quickly should a relapse occur.

Following is a brief review of three RP models. The reader can consult the references if interested in any of these or other specific models of SUDs treatment or approach to RP.

Addict Aftercare Model (N.I.D.A.)

This RP model was developed through the collaboration of researchers in the United States and Hong Kong. They adapted an aftercare model used in Hong Kong to treating opiate addicts in the U.S. Goals were to reduce relapse with drug abusers by developing aftercare treatment aimed at promoting lifestyle change. One result of this project was a descriptive manual that gives instructions on how to carry out a structured aftercare program that systematically addresses the need for lifestyle changes. This model presumes that besides being a disease, SUDs are a way of life with a distinct subculture. Recovery requires the addicted person to stop drug use and develop a new way of life. Developing a new way of life requires learning new skills.

This model states that the addict faces a number of "recovery challenges" and needs "skills" to avoid relapsing. To remain sober, the client must learn to:

- Handle drug cravings.
- Socialize differently in order to build a new social network.
- Adjust to drug-free activities and satisfactions.
- Cope with physical pain or stress without returning to drug use.
- Initiate and sustain relationships to meet intimacy needs.
- Refuse drug use offers.
- Respond to "slips" to prevent a full-blown relapse.

This program consists of recovery training sessions, fellowship meetings, drug-free social and community activities, and a network of senior ex-addicts. Each of these components is discussed in detail in the treatment manual describing this RP approach. Like other RP models, this one addresses the reality of relapse, recommending that clients discuss this possibility <u>before</u> trouble arises. Honest reporting of actual drug-use episodes is encouraged. Problems should be confronted directly and the members should be aware of signs of trouble. Assessing actual relapses and discussing these in group sessions helps the person develop strategies to stop drug use. Honest sharing can help the entire group learn from the experience of individuals who relapse frequently.

All of the group session topics fall into one of the following four categories.

Being clean. The seven topics of this section deal with the most direct threats to abstinence and issues of drug use. The topics include: de-addiction and craving; your dangerous situations; a drink, a toke–risks and limits; saying no; coping with pain and prescription medication; relating to active drug users; and tips about slips.

Highs and lows. The three topics of this section offer help with stressful events and anxieties associated with finding new pleasures in the first year or two of abstinence. The topics include: having good times without drugs; preparing for stressful situations; and coping with pain and prescription medication.

Social relations. Nine topics help recovering clients explore the social problems that are likely to confront them, including: assessing your social life; making a new friend; a more open recovery; love and intimate relations; issues of the recovering family; the goals of group membership; having the best group we can; relating to active drug users; recovery and community service.

Work and growth. The six topics on work and growth help the recovering person consider how performing a certain role in a straight world affects recovery. Topics include: phases of recovery; presenting your past for employment; a job that meets your needs; handling on-the-job problems; recovering and community service; looking ahead–plans, goals, and dreams.

Although this manual was developed for an aftercare program for opiate addicts, the topics lend themselves to easy adoption by rehabilitation programs, halfway houses, therapeutic communities and outpatient programs for any type of SUDs. These topics are also adaptable to both individual and group sessions. There are many ways the clinician can use his or her experience and creativity to accomplish this.

Research showed that aftercare group members had better rates of abstinence or "rare" uses of opioids at the one-year follow-up period compared to members of the control group. This program also helped some of the unemployed participants find jobs.

Cognitive Behavioral Model

The late Dr. G. Alan Marlatt from the Addictive Behaviors Research Center at the University of Washington was the first researcher to address the problem of relapse and propose RP strategies for clinicians, as well as integrate "mindfulness" strategies popular in today's treatment environment into an iteration of RP called mindfulness-based relapse prevention (MBRP), which was a collaboration with Drs. Sarah Bowen and Neha Chawla. His work resulted in one of the most comprehensive theoretical and clinical models of RP, which influenced many researchers and clinicians over several decades. This model has been adapted and applied to disorders such as impulse control problems and impulsive aggressive acts in addition to addictive disorders. This work is described in many publications, including the classic book entitled *Relapse Prevention: A Self-Control Strategy for the Maintenance of Behavior Change* Dr. Marlatt collaborated with Dr. Judith Gordon and others for the first edition of this book, and with Dr. Dennis Donovan and others for the updated version of this classic book. This is one of the most widely cited references in the literature on relapse. Dr. Marlatt is considered by many as a leading authority on RP.

According to Dr. Marlatt, RP is a "self-management program" to help a person maintain changes such as abstaining from substance use (or gambling or other addictive or compulsive behaviors). This approach engages the client as a co-therapist, giving her the primary responsibility for change. Recovery is a "learning task" that involves acquiring new skills. This model of RP is predicated on key assumptions about behavior change. The first assumption is that the causes of an addictive habit and the process of behavior change are governed by different principles. Second, stopping addictive use of alcohol or other drugs involves three stages:

- Making a commitment and becoming motivated to change.
- Implementing the change.
- Long-term maintenance of change.

Marlatt identified multiple determinants of relapse. These fall into one of the two general categories, *intra*personal and *inter*personal factors. Examples of *intra*personal factors are negative emotional states, motivation, coping, outcome expectancies, craving, and self-efficacy. Examples of *inter*personal factors include social pressures to use substances, and conflicts in relationships.

The rationale behind such a categorization is to help addicted people identify which of these factors is "high risk" or threatens their recovery. A high-risk situation is defined as "any situation which poses a threat to the individual's sense of control and increases the risk of potential relapse." Someone may fail to cope with high-risk situations because coping skills are lacking, fear and anxiety inhibit a positive coping response, or the situation was not recognized early enough. Relapse episodes often follow *unexpected* high-risk situations, or those the client is unprepared for. Sometimes the person may "set-up" the relapse in which the relapse is the last link in a chain of events.

Assessing high-risk situations involves two stages. First, the clinician helps the client identify situations posing future relapse risk. Self-monitoring records such as the daily drinking diary, self-efficacy ratings, autobiographical statements and a review of past relapses can be used to assess risks. The second stage involves assessing the client's coping skills through naturalistic observation of the client in an actual problem situation. Simulations and role-playing can also be used to assess these skills.

Three cognitive factors interact in the relapse process according to Dr. Marlatt. These are self-efficacy, outcome expectancy and attribution of causality.

Self-efficacy is the client's judgment about how well he deals with difficult, stressful or high risk situations.

Outcome expectancies are the anticipated outcomes of a given behavior. If a client expects the outcome of substance use to be positive, the probability of relapse increases.

Attribution of causality refers to the client's perception of whether substance use was caused by internal or external factors. This has an impact on subsequent behavior. If a client uses substances one time and believes he has lost control of his disease rather than accepting that a mistake was made, he is more likely to continue drug use.

Recovery can address each client's unique high-risk factors. The clinician should strive for a balance between verbal and non-verbal techniques such as imagery, meditation and exercise. This model stresses the need for both specific and global RP strategies such as skill training, cognitive reframing strategies and lifestyle interventions. Cognitive or behavior coping skills to deal with "high-risk" relapse situations can be taught in individual or group situations. If these new skills are learned, then the probability of relapse decreases. Since teaching addicted clients explicit skills or cognitive strategies to cope with high-risk situations is not always enough to prevent relapse, clinicians need other "global" or self-control strategies, such as substitute indulgences, exercise, relaxation, meditation, self-hypnosis and learning to develop a "balanced" daily lifestyle. Modifying one's lifestyle is critical in overcoming a SUD.

A broader purpose of RP is to ease changes in personal habits and lifestyle to reduce the risk of physical disease or psychological stress. The aim is to teach the client to prevent unhealthy habits by balancing work and play, and by developing positive habits. Achieving this requires a balance between the external demands or "should" activities, and those the person "wants" to engage in for pleasure or fulfillment.

The clinician can assess sources of stress in the client's life and the client's health status, exercise habits, relaxation practices, use of drugs or medications including caffeine, interpersonal activities and religious beliefs. Based on the assessment of these areas, the clinician can help the client develop a program for lifestyle change. This RP approach advocates teaching clients moderation when approaching lifestyle changes.

The person's reaction to an initial lapse is a crucial determinant of whether a "full-blown" relapse will occur. Initially using a substance after a period of abstinence is seen as a "lapse," or a "transitional process," that may lead to a return to previous levels of substance use. The client who lapses can be compared with a person at a "fork in the road," one path leading to the former problem level of substance use and, the other path leading toward positive change. A lapse can represent an opportunity for growth, a useful learning experience. Therefore, clinicians should teach clients to anticipate and cope with "slips" or lapses to prevent full-blown relapses.

Psychoeducational

This RP approach evolved from Daley's collaboration with Dr. Marlatt, and his review of the empirical and clinical literature, extensive treatment experiences and designing and conducting treatment groups. This model operationalizes many of Marlatt's concepts and includes an interactive workbook for clients that helps them to personalize information reviewed and to develop an RP plan.

Conducting this program in group sessions provides an opportunity to use the group process so that clients can give and receive feedback from peers and learn from each other. RP groups are "task-oriented" and involve brief lectures and discussions, and the use of dyads (two clients) or small groups to complete tasks that focus on a specific RP topic. However, all of these RP strategies can be used in individual sessions.

The goals are to educate clients about relapse, help them learn coping strategies to manage relapse risk factors and warning signs, and help them learn how to interrupt an actual relapse should one occur. This model views a SUD as a biopsychosocial illness with multiple etiologies and effects. Recovery is a long-term process of abstinence and change which can be difficult and painful in the early stages. The recovery needs of each client depend on: the length and severity of the SUDs; age, gender, and ethnicity; and the degree of damage resulting from the SUDs. Relapse is a multifaceted process resulting from a combination of affective, behavioral, cognitive, interpersonal, physiological, psychological, spiritual, and treatment-related variables. For many, relapse is part of the total recovery journey. Relapses often can be learning experiences and help recovery.

RP groups are designed to actively involve the participants in lectures, discussions, role-plays, and small task-oriented activities. The *Relapse Prevention Workbook* provides the content for the sessions. Homework tasks are sometimes assigned between group sessions.

Sessions can last one to two hours. Chapter 5 of this book provides an overview of RP groups and provides 12 sessions:

- The process and domains of recovery
- Cravings and urges to use substances
- Managing anger
- Managing boredom
- Refusing substance use offers
- Establishing a recovery support system
- How mutual support programs aid recovery and reduce relapse risk
- Identifying and managing relapse warning signs
- Identifying and managing high risk situations
- Maintaining recovery by using tools in daily life
- Setbacks: managing a lapse or relapse
- Creating a balanced lifestyle

RESEARCH SUPPORT FOR RP WITH SUBSTANCE USE DISORDERS

As stated earlier, all treatments for SUDs aim to reduce the risk of relapse. Outcome studies show that many behavioral, medication and combined treatments are effective in doing this even though many clients relapse once or more due to the chronic nature of addictive disease. And, many treatments of SUDs incorporate strategies from the RP literature to focus on determinants of relapse (high risk factors) and warning signs of relapse for individuals in recovery.

However, there is also clinical and research literature specific to RP (also called relapse prevention therapy, RPT). Literature reviews, results from numerous single-site and multi-site clinical trials, and meta-analyses of findings from multiple studies show that RP is effective in improving recovery and reducing relapse rates of individuals with SUDs. A brief description of RPT and findings from clinical trials can be found on the Substance Abuse and Mental Health Administration's (SAMHSA) National Registry of Evidenced-based Programs and Practices.

Following is a brief summary of research findings:

Review of randomized trials: Carroll reviewed 24 randomized controlled clinical trials of RP among smokers, alcohol abusers, marijuana abusers, cocaine abusers, opiate addicts, and other drug abusers. She reports that RP is superior to no-treatment control groups, especially with smokers. Carroll also reports that RP holds the greatest promise in helping the addicted individual maintain gains after stopping substance use and reducing the severity of relapses when they occur. Clients with higher levels of psychiatric and SUD severity appear to benefit most from RP. Thus, RP may be especially helpful for clients with co-occurring psychiatric disorders.

Meta-analysis of clinical trials: Irvin and colleagues conducted a meta-analysis of 26 clinical trials on RP with a total sample of almost 10,000 participants. The RP approach used in these studies was consistent with Marlatt's cognitive-behavioral approach to RP. Irvin found that the strongest treatment effect for RP was with patients who had problems with alcohol or polysubstance use. They also found that individual, group and marital modalities appeared to be equally effective, and that medication is very helpful in reducing relapse rates, particularly for the treatment of alcohol problems.

RP delivered in groups: Several studies found that RP administered in groups is as efficacious as RP delivered in individual sessions. McKay and colleagues randomized cocaine users to standard group or RP individual sessions, and found that those who endorsed a goal of total abstinence when entering treatment had better treatment outcomes in RP than those in standard group counseling.

RP including spouses: Several studies included spouses in the RP intervention. Maisto and colleagues' study of the first relapse episodes and reasons for terminating relapses of men with alcoholism who were treated with their spouses found that the relapses of clients receiving RP in addition to behavioral marital therapy were shorter than those of clients not receiving the RP. In a study of married alcoholics, O'Farrell found that in couples assessed to be "high distress," abstinence rates at 12-months were highest for those who received behavioral marital therapy (BMT) in combination with RP. Alcoholics who received RP after completing BMT had more abstinent days, fewer days drinking and, for those with the poorest functioning at baseline, improved marriages compared to those who received only BMT.

Delayed effects of RP among cocaine abusers and smokers: Carroll and colleagues compared cocaine abusers receiving RP to those receiving interpersonal psychotherapy (IPT). RP was more effective than IPT for clients with more severe cocaine problems and to some extent for those with higher psychiatric severity. In another outpatient study of cocaine abusers, Carroll and colleagues compared RP to a operationalized clinical management and medication (desipramine: a tricyclic antidepressant or placebo). At one year follow-up, they found a delayed improved response to treatment for patients who received RP. Rawson and colleagues found a similar "sleeper effect" for RP with cocaine addicts. Goldstein and colleagues also found a significant delayed effect for an experimental RP condition compared to an educational support control condition at six months for smokers treated in a 10-week group program. These findings of *delayed effects* of RP are consistent with the idea that learning new ways to cope with high risk situations takes time for the client with a substance use disorder.

RP with alcohol problems: Saunders and Allsop found that male subjects receiving RP returned to problematic alcohol use at a rate of four to seven times less rapidly than subjects in a discussion control group at the six-month follow-up period. Chaney and O'Leary compared subjects receiving RP skills training to those receiving a discussion control group at 12-months. They found that subjects receiving RP drank less, had fewer episodes of intoxication, experienced less severe lapses for shorter periods of time, and stopped drinking significantly sooner after a relapse compared to clients in control condition. The mean number of "days drunk" and "total number of drinks" were significantly lower with

RP. Koski-James found that there was greater treatment adherence and satisfaction, reduced lengths of inpatient treatment, and fewer alcohol related arrests among clients receiving RP compared to clients receiving other treatment modalities. Ito and colleagues found that hospitalized alcoholic clients receiving RP drank on fewer days, drank less alcohol, were more likely to complete a course of aftercare treatment, and had a slightly higher rate of continuous abstinence at 6-month follow-up compared to clients who received interpersonal therapy.

Medication combined with counseling: Kranzler assessed the effects of the antidepressant fluoxetine as an adjunct to RP in alcoholics and found that both fluoxetine and placebo groups decreased their number of drinking days and drinks per drinking day six months after treatment. Since there were no significant differences between the fluoxetine or placebo groups, the conclusion of Kranzler was that RP was a factor in improved drinking outcomes. O'Malley found that patients who received RP and naltrexone were less likely to relapse to heavy drinking after a lapse when compared to a control group. Many studies funded by the National Institute on Drug Abuse, including the Clinical Trials Network project, show positive outcomes of medications, which usually are provided with counseling or therapy.

Findings from the Relapse Replication and Extension Project (RREP): This was a multisite replication and extension study of Marlatt's RP model funded by the National Institute on Alcohol Abuse and Alcoholism. The RREP addressed the relationship between a high-risk situation and relapse to alcohol use. Several changes were recommended to the taxonomy of high-risk situations as well as increased emphasis on factors that make some people more vulnerable to relapse regardless of the relapse situation. Negative emotional states, social pressure to drink, physical withdrawal, craving, urges and substance-related cues are the most common high-risk situations for relapse. The availability of coping skills is a protective factor against relapse, and the use of ineffective coping is a consistent predictor of relapse.

The availability and use of adequate coping skills and higher levels of self-efficacy may prevent a crisis situation from turning into a relapse. Many factors may precipitate a relapse. Factors that occur closer in time to a relapse (e.g., conflict with spouse) account for a substantially greater amount of variance in subsequent outcome than the relapse factors that are identified at intake (e.g., family history of substance use disorder). Also, the type of relapse that may occur in the future is not necessarily related to the type of the most recent relapse.

Limitations to Studies and Reviews of RP for Substance Use Disorders

There are several limitations to studies and reviews on RP. First, there is no consensus on when or how to define or measure relapse. For example, should this be measured during active treatment, at specified follow-up points in time (e.g., 3, 6, 12, 24 months)? Many clinical trials have short follow-up periods of less than 6 months, so long-term outcome is not studied. Also, should the "primary" substance represent the main relapse outcome measure? In terms of how to measure relapse some of the possibilities include: time to first lapse or relapse; time to "heavy" or "regular" use of a substance (note: it is easier to define "heavy" alcohol use compared to drug use), days of substance use, amount of substance use, etc. Clinical studies usually evaluate outcome in terms of substance use as well as changes in functioning or quality of life.

Second, some studies have used RP as the single treatment intervention for cessation of substance use rather than for maintenance of change once substance use was stopped. In the real world of clinical care, RP is usually integrated into the overall treatment plan. The interventions discussed in this book may be delivered at different stages of treatment.

Third, studies usually do not differentiate between subjects who are motivated to change substance use behavior and those who have little or no motivation to change (e.g., they may enter treatment due to external pressure from the legal system, an employer, or a family member). Clinicians understand that clients vary in their level of motivation to change. They also know that motivational strategies are often needed in the early stages of recovery to help engage clients in treatment and influence their desire to deal with their substance problems.

Fourth, in some studies sample sizes are small and there in not enough power to detect statistical differences between experimental and control conditions. Meta analyses that combine results from multiple studies are one way to use data from multiple studies.

Fifth, studies do not always use random assignment or operationalize the therapy being compared against RP, making it difficult to determine what factors contribute to treatment effects. In more recent clinical trials, comparison groups (usually called "usual care" or "treatment-as-usual") are used against which to compare clients receiving the intervention.

And last, the follow-up period to study relapse following a period of treatment is often short-term. Clinicians would prefer longer term follow-up periods (several years), but the high cost of conducting studies often limits follow up periods to a year or less.

APPROACHES TO RECOVERY AND RP FOR PSYCHIATRIC OR CO-OCCURRING DISORDERS

Recovery

There are many models of recovery from psychiatric and co-occurring disorders. While definitions and domains of recovery may vary across these models, recovery is viewed as a long-term process of managing one's psychiatric disorder(s) and changing oneself and lifestyle, which often leads to wellness, improved functioning and a better quality of life. A revised definition from SAMHSA states that "recovery from mental disorders (and/or SUDs) is a process of change through which individuals improve their health and wellness, live a self-directed life, and strive to reach their full potential." This includes four major dimensions of health, home, purpose and community. Components of recovery according to SAMHSA include:

Hope: The belief that a person can change, get better and improve their life.

Self-directed: The client chooses paths to recovery and has a major say in the treatment plan and methods of recovery (with input from professionals, family or others).

Empowerment: The client feels positive change and recovery are possible if actions are taken to manage his disorder(s) and use skills to manage the challenges of recovery.

Respect: The client increases self respect. And, very importantly, the client expects respect from professionals who provide care rather than moralistic and pejorative approach.

Responsibility: While many people can help clients, it is ultimately their responsibility to engage in recovery and work at improving their lives.

Individualized plan: Each client has a plan that addresses his or her specific disorders, problems, needs and desires.

Strength-based: Focus goes beyond symptoms and problems, and resilience and other positive qualities or achievements of clients are recognized and valued.

Non-linear: Setbacks occur, clients have ups and downs, and recovery does not take a continuous linear path. Some areas may improve while others do not. Or, some areas may change significantly while other areas show only minor changes.

Holistic: Recovery focuses on all domains of life and incorporates help from many professional, mutual support and community sources.

Peer support: Clients help each other by sharing their hopes, strength and what has helped them cope with their disorder(s). Peers have much to offer each other as they have struggled and experienced psychiatric disorders as well as recovery and wellness.

Gingerich and Mueser, and Ralph and Corrigan refer to objective and subjective elements of recovery from psychiatric illness which overlap with those of SAMHSA. *Objective* aspects include improved role functioning (work, school, home, parenting) and being part of a community, healthy and satisfying social relationships, involvement in leisure and recreational activities, and independent living (when possible). *Subjective* aspects of recovery include having a sense of purpose in life, feeling optimistic about life or managing one's disorder(s), self-determination, feeling motivated to work at recovery and improve oneself, having a sense of curiosity and achieving a state of well-being.

Factors impacting on recovery include severity of psychiatric illness, presence of a substance use disorder, family and social support, social and cognitive skills, and access to treatment, other services, and mutual support programs.

We conducted a survey on 168 patients with co-occurring disorders as part of a clinical quality improvement initiative asking them to rate and identify the challenges they face in recovery. In order of priority, clients identified the following recovery challenges.

Managing emotions or moods: Some clients need to learn global emotion management strategies. Others need to learn strategies to cope with specific emotions or moods such as anger, anxiety, boredom, depression, emptiness, guilt and shame, and loneliness.

Family and social relationships: Clients identified the need to deal with the effects of disorders on relationships and when possible, to get the family or significant other in treatment and/or recovery. They also identified the importance of social support in recovery (mutual support programs, involvement in the community).

People, places, events: The impact of direct and indirect social pressures was identified as a major challenge to recovery (high risk people, places, events). Clients need to be aware of these, as well as their impact on thinking, emotions and actions. And, they need skills to avoid or cope with high risk people, places or events.

Lifestyle issues: Clients acknowledged the need to make changes in their lifestyle (healthcare, exercise habits, how they spend time).

Thinking: The impact of negative or "stinking" thinking was identified as a challenge that impacts on recovery and relapse. Distorted thinking contributes to depression, anxiety and other problems among clients, so it is important to learn cognitive strategies to change and alter their thinking.

Other issues identified as recovery challenges include personality issues such as stubbornness or self-centeredness (called "character defects" in 12-step programs), cravings for substances, triggers for relapse, the need to focus on spirituality and the importance of involvement in 12-step programs such as Alcoholics Anonymous, Narcotics Anonymous or Dual Recovery Anonymous.

Illness and Symptom Management

Illness Management and Recovery (IMR) developed by Gingerich and Mueser, and the Symptom Management Module develped by Liberman are comprehensive approaches to treatment and relapse prevention for chronic, severe and persistent types of psychiatric illness such as schizophrenia and other psychotic disorders, bipolar illness, chronic or recurrent forms of depression or other chronic mental disorders. The goals of these approaches are to help clients manage their disorder(s), reduce the impact of psychiatric symptoms on their lives, reduce relapses and hospitalizations, engage in long-term recovery and improve the quality of life.

These approaches use a variety of educational and therapeutic strategies in individual, group or family sessions to actively engage clients in recovery by teaching skills and assigning therapy tasks related to their specific goals. Clinicians may help promote recovery and reduce relapse risk by helping the client:

Become educated about illness and recovery: Provide information on types, causes, symptoms, effects, and treatment and management of specific disorders (medications, electroconvulsive and other medical treatments; therapy or counseling; psychiatric rehabilitation; case management; vocational services; and other services), recovery from psychiatric illness or co-occurring disorders, relapse, family issues and support systems.

Adhere to treatment: Use motivational and other strategies to increase the client's likelihood of taking medications as prescribed, and attending treatment sessions or recovery activities. Clients who adhere to their treatment do better than those who are poorly adherent.

Manage symptoms of psychiatric illness: Teach clients to monitor and manage acute and persistent symptoms of illness so that they feel more in control of their recovery, and take action to reduce the likelihood of more severe relapses should early warning signs occur. For example, a client with auditory hallucinations may be taught relaxation or deep breathing techniques to decrease arousal. Or, the client may be taught to use positive self talk ("I can handle these voices."). *Develop coping skills to change thinking and behaviors, and manage emotions or moods and stress:* teach social skills, stress management, problem solving skills and/or cognitive skills to help clients reduce symptoms, negative emotions or moods and stress, and improve their mental health

- Learning to examine and challenge thoughts and beliefs that contribute to negative feelings or emotions or problems can lead to the client feeling more in control and less anxious or depressed.

- Learning to plan daily and weekly activities can reduce boredom and help the client feel more involved in social and leisure activities that are meaningful and enjoyable.

Involve the family or significant other: Many clients live with their family or others who are significant in their lives. Family psychoeducation and family therapy are helpful with psychiatric or co-occurring disorders. Family interventions help families learn to understand and support their ill family member as well as learn ways to cope with their own struggles and the emotional burden that is common when a loved one has a psychiatric or co-occurring disorder.

Develop a support system: Social support and connections with other people can aid a client's recovery and improve quality of life. Some clients may need help learning social or conversational skills so they are able to interact with others. Others may need help in reaching out and asking others for help and support for a problem or engaging in a social or leisure activity. Clinicians can help by linking clients with mutual support programs, recovery clubs, drop-in centers or other community services.

Identify and manage early warning signs of psychiatric relapse: This may involve learning about common warning signs as well as signs specific to a given client based on diagnoses. For example, cutting down or stopping medications, treatment sessions or participation in recovery activities often precedes relapse for many clients regardless of their diagnoses. However, clients also have signs that may be unique to them or specific to their psychiatric disorder. Warning sign management may also involve others who support the client (e.g., health care providers, family or significant others, peers in recovery).

Learn how alcohol or drug use or substance use disorders impact on psychiatric illness or recovery: Clients with substance use disorders (SUD) benefit from integrated treatment that focuses on both types of disorders. Since each disorder affects the other, clients need help focusing on both disorders. In addition, clients who drink heavily or use illicit drugs can suffer adverse consequences even if they don't meet criteria for a SUD. For example, smoking a joint can contribute to hallucinations or feelings of paranoia for a client with a psychotic disorder or borderline personality disorder. Heavy drinking can lead to attempts to hurt oneself or others. Clients can benefit from monitoring substance use and effects of use on symptoms and functioning, learning to identify and manage triggers to use substances, and learning skills to resist social pressure to drink or use drugs.

Other Approaches to Co-Occurring Disorders

Many clinical researchers have developed protocols to address various manifestations of co-occurring disorders or specific combinations of disorders. Some of these approaches were initially developed for a specific disorder, then expanded to address clinical needs of different disorders. All emphasize the need to address substance use disorders. For the interested reader, treatment protocols, therapy or counseling manuals, client recovery materials, and/or recovery videos are available from NIDA, NIAAA and many publishers.

RESEARCH SUPPORT FOR TREATMENT OF
PSYCHIATRIC OR CO-OCCURRING DISORDERS

Many studies of psychiatric illness or co-occurring disorders document positive effects of treatment including reduced rates of relapse and psychiatric hospitalizations in many, but not all of the studies reviewed. Following are a few examples of finding from specific studies, meta-analyses of multiple studies, and literature reviews:

- Accordint to Ralph and Corrigan, ten long-term studies of schizophrenia conducted in the U.S., Germany, Japan and Switzerland with an average follow-up of 15 years or more found significant rates of recovery or improvement, ranging from 36% to 77%. Some clients experienced brief symptoms lasting days or weeks with minimal adverse impact on social or occupational functioning.

- Three studies of illness management and recovery (IMR) conducted in three different countries with 354 clients found greater improvements in illness self management skills for clients receiving IMR compared to usual care. Gingerich and Mueser reported that these clients had greater reductions of psychiatric symptoms and more improvements in psychosocial functioning.

- A meta-analysis of 34 studies of cognitive-behavioral therapy (CBT) for psychotic disorders by Wykes and collegues showed moderate improvements in psychotic symptoms, negative symptoms, overall functioning, and mood symptoms. Both individual and group CBT approaches were comparable in their effects on outcome.

- Reviews of studies and meta-analyses of social skills training (SST) by Liberman, Bellack and colleagues, and Kurtz and Mueser show that target behaviors such as conversations, friendship, intimacy, leisure activities, work, community living and substance abuse show improvements in all of these areas. There are mixed results in regards to SST reducing relapse rates.

- Studies by Mueser and colleagues, and McFarlane of family psychoeducation or family therapy show improved recovery rates and fewer hospitalizations for members with psychiatric disorder(s) as well as improvement for family members such as reduced burden and improved coping skills.

Many of the cognitive and behavioral interventions described in models of RP approaches can be used with clients who have substance use and other addictive disorders, psychiatric disorders, and co-occurring disorders. RP interventions aim to help clients maintain change over time and address the most common issues contributing to the increased risk of relapse. RP also aims to help clients make lifestyle changes that reduce stress and facilitate personal growth and satisfaction.

Studies indicate that RP reduces relapse rates and the severity of lapses or relapses. RP strategies can be used throughout the continuum of care. In addition, family members can be included in sessions and involved in the development of RP plans for members with a SUD. Medication-assisted treatment for opioid, alcohol or nicotine use disorders added to RP is also helpful to some clients.

Many of the RP approaches described in the literature are short-term or brief treatments and can be provided in individual or group sessions, making them attractive and cost effective. The majority of clinical models of RP are supported by user-friendly, interactive recovery materials such as books, workbooks, videos and audiotapes. These supplemental materials provide additional information and support to clients who can learn to use self-management techniques of RP on their own, following completion of formal treatment.

Individuals with severe psychiatric illness and SUDs have increased vulnerability for relapse because of multiple complex issues, including housing problems, social and cognitive deficits, and poor support systems. An integrated approach to treatment is optimal in addressing CODs. Treating one condition improves outcomes of treating the other condition. Integrating pharmacotherapy with psychosocial interventions is beneficial in improving both disorders. Incorporating strategies to enhance treatment entry and improve adherence to treatment in individuals with CODs should be an integral part of comprehensive treatment planning. Interventions targeting psychiatric symptom management and early identification of psychiatric relapse signs, and the use of medications to reduce depressive and anxiety manifestations are critical to minimize the risk of relapse.

CHAPTER 3

Counseling Strategies to Promote Recovery and Reduce Relapse Risk

The clinical strategies described in this chapter can be used in individual or group sessions. Some can be used with families.

The use of experiential learning or action techniques such as role playing or behavioral rehearsal, monodramas, bibliotherapy, use of workbooks, a daily inventory, interactive videos and homework assignments makes learning an active experience. Such techniques can enhance the client's self-awareness, decrease defensiveness and encourage behavioral change.

In RP groups, action techniques provide the opportunity to elicit feedback and support for clients from their peers, identify common relapse themes and issues, and practice specific cognitive or interpersonal skills. For example, the group leader sets up a role-play in which a male cocaine addict in recovery is offered cocaine by another addict who is not in recovery. Other group members are instructed to imagine that they are also in this situation and to pay close attention to their thoughts and feelings as they observe the role-play. Although the client refuses the substance offer during the actual role-play, the post-role play review reveals several interesting facts:

- First, the client's body language and affect during the role play are viewed by observers as giving mixed messages to the other addict offering the drug, thus opening the door for the person to continue to pressure the addicted person to use drugs.

- Group members believe that ambivalence about sobriety is easily perceived by other addicts offering substances. Second, although the client refuses the offer to use the drug, his internal dialogue is much more ambivalent, and strong thoughts of getting high on cocaine emerge. This takes the client by surprise because he feels his commitment to abstinence is strong.

- When other group members share their reactions regarding what it is like imagining being in this situation, it becomes apparent that the majority feel that such interpersonal encounters tap the "addicted part" of them that still wants to use substances. While some clients are not surprised by this, others are.

Such experiential learning often teaches clients to look beneath the surface and examine internal thoughts, feelings and desires. Once clients are aware of these, the clinician can then help them explore, develop and practice strategies to manage social pressures they expect to face.

The strategies discussed in the remainder of this chapter are adapted from the various models of RP as well as other treatment models that incorporate relapse issues into treatment. Strategies are clustered in the categories of treatment acceptance and adherence, illness management, relapse prevention and intervention skills, emotional management skills, relationship skills and support systems, cognitive coping skills and lifestyle issues.

MOTIVATION TO CHANGE

Address Ambivalence and Motivational Struggles

- Ambivalence regarding treatment participation or change is normal. Accept and appreciate small changes a client makes.
- Anticipate non-adherence at various stages of treatment and discuss any prior history of poor adherence.
- Discuss immediately any motivational struggles and adherence problems that the client may be experiencing.
- Use strategies from motivational interviewing to help enhance a client's motivation to change and engage in treatment or recovery.

Therapeutic Relationship

- Understand the importance of your relationship with your client (and group), express empathy and concern, convey helpfulness in your attitudes and behaviors, encourage the client to discuss the counseling process and the client-counselor relationship.
- If you conduct groups, periodically ask the members how the group is doing, what they find helpful and what changes they would like to see in the group.

Treatment Preparation

- Prepare the client for group and what it will entail. Encourage the client to listen and learn from peers, self-disclose personal feelings and problems, and give and get support from peers.
- Explore the client's hopes and expectations for treatment and any resistance or barriers to treatment.
- Discuss pros and cons of treatment from the client's perspective, and prepare the client for what occurs in various forms of treatment (e.g., group therapy, an intensive outpatient program, medication management, or a specific form of counseling).

Treatment Plan Development

- Negotiate rather than dictate the treatment plan.
- Emphasize to the client that it is her responsibility to change.
- Review goals and progress regularly, discussing pros and cons of abstinence as a goal.
- Since no one type of treatment is appropriate for all clients, provide options regarding treatment.

If a client does not accept the treatment that you recommend at this time, negotiate a plan in which the client agrees to this treatment in the future if his or her preferred treatment plan does not work. For example, I (dcd) worked with a nurse who had an SUD and serious depressive illness that I thought required medication. She initially refused to consider medications for her mood disorder. However, she agreed to reconsider this option if her mood did not improve over the next several weeks. Despite becoming sober from alcohol and remaining so, her mood improved only slightly over a period of two months. She then reluctantly agreed to see our program psychiatrist and to take an antidepressant that was prescribed, which led to a significant mood improvement. As her mood improved she reported her recovery from alcoholism went better and she felt her life was much improved.

Treatment Process

- Use evidence-based practices, change treatment frequency or intensity as needed, give the client feedback about her problems and progress, discuss her reaction to this feedback, and provide reinforcement for treatment adherence.

- Address social anxiety regarding group participation. For example, we had an elderly woman (one of the few clients who cussed me out in my office over the years) with chronic social anxiety and depression who was dependent on alcohol and benzodiazepines. Once our outpatient treatment team was able to wean her off the benzodiazepines and get her on an SSRI to help her depression and anxiety, she became more stable and able to use therapy. Her social anxiety decreased as a result of medications and our work in therapy, and she was able to join a treatment group and attend AA meetings. Several years after she moved to another state to be closer to her family, she called to update me. She was still taking medications and seeing a therapist and psychiatrist for maintenance treatment every several months and was still active in AA.

System Strategies

- Develop a clinic or program policy on adherence to both prescribed medications and therapy appointments (including group sessions).

- Establish program and clinician benchmarks for acceptable levels of client adherence to scheduled treatment sessions.. For example, one of our clinics established an acceptable show rate for outpatient appointments and had clinicians review adherence rates with a supervisor regularly. This led to a greater awareness of adherence problems and clinic changes such as calling to remind new clients of appointments, and clinicians following up with clients who missed appointments. A result was improved adherence rates.

- Conduct regular satisfaction surveys with clients and families. Find out what is helpful and what they think could be changed or improved upon.

- Provide easy access to treatment for clients and offer flexible appointment times.

- Use prompts or phone reminders regarding appointments, especially for new clients and those with histories of poor compliance.

- Reach out to poorly adherent clients to get them back in treatment as soon as possible after they fail to show.

- Use case management services for more chronically impaired clients.

ADHERENCE AND RETENTION IN TREATMENT AND RECOVERY PROGRAMS

Woody Allen once said, "80% of success is showing up!" This speaks to the importance of adherence. Poor adherence to treatment services or recovery activities is a major factor in relapse. On the other hand, good adherence increases the odds of recovery and decreases the chances of a relapse. *If the client shows up, you can help!* Even if the client is struggling with motivation to change, using substances or having other problems, you can help them if they attend their sessions. For example, I had a client who I was seeing in outpatient treatment (following a rehab program) for alcohol dependence. After our fifth weekly session he told me, "I didn't tell you the truth last week when you asked if I had drunk any alcohol. I drank twice in the past two weeks." I thanked him for sharing this with me and we used it to discuss several important issues: factors that contributed to his alcohol lapse, how to stop this lapse now, what it was like for him to share the truth, and how being open about any episodes of use would be necessary for treatment to work. I believe this was a critical point in our therapy as he told me later he was watching closely for my reaction to his use of alcohol and wondering if I would confront him. Following completion of individual (and some marital sessions) treatment he continued in AA and the last I heard he had over five years of continuous sobriety and was still active in AA.

Many studies show that clients who adhere to treatment show better outcomes and lower relapse rates compared to those who do not adhere to treatment, miss sessions or drop out early. The following strategies can help you improve adherence to treatment among your addicted clients.

Incorporate Strategies to Improve Adherence

Many studies show that motivational incentives improve substance use outcomes and adherence behaviors among clients. Incentives are usually used to reward abstinence from alcohol or other drugs, but they can also be used to reward adherence to treatment sessions. For example, in one of our acute partial hospital programs for clients with SUDs (including those with a co-occurring psychiatric disorder), clients earned draws from a fishbowl for each day of program attendance and extra bonus points for attending the program on consecutive days. At the end of each week, clients drew slips from a fishbowl; about half had an encouraging saying written on them (good job; keep coming back) and the other half listed small, medium or large prizes. Small prizes were valued at $2 of less; medium prizes at about $5; and large prizes at $10 or more. The result of using incentives was that attendance increased by 60%.

Facilitate the Transition Between Levels of Care

Clients can make significant gains in residential or hospital treatment programs only to have these negated due to failure to adhere to ongoing residential, ambulatory or aftercare treatment. The transition between inpatient and ambulatory care is an important area upon which to focus clinical interventions. Interventions used to enhance treatment entry and adherence that lower the risk of relapse include:

- Prior to discharge from inpatient treatment, have a single session using a motivational approach. In one of our quality improvement surveys, we found that a single motivational therapy (MT) session provided to hospitalized psychiatric patients with co-occurring substance use disorders led to a nearly two-fold increase in the show rate for the initial outpatient appointment.) A study by Swanson and colleagues found that hospitalized patients with schizophrenia and substance use disorders who received a single motivational session prior to hospital discharge more than doubled their initial aftercare entry rates. Clients who show for their initial appointment have a reduced risk of treatment dropout and subsequent psychiatric and/or substance use relapse.

- Use telephone or mail reminders of initial treatment appointments.
- If possible, connect with a staff member from the program the client will be attending although this is often difficult due to logistics (programs in different physical locations).

MEDICATION-ASSISTED TREATMENT

Offer Medications Options

Prolonged substance use can cause alterations in brain chemistry, which can be helped with medications. Medications for SUDs may disrupt the reward provided by alcohol or drugs or affect the dysregulation of brain chemistry caused by substances.

The use of medication-assisted treatment reduces the client's use of substances, decreases the risk of transmitting or acquiring hepatitis B or C or HIV, increases retention in treatment, and enhances the health of these individuals. For pregnant mothers, medication can lead to improved birth outcomes for babies.

Medications should be combined with therapy or a psychosocial treatment program. They can be especially helpful for clients with a history of multiple relapses to alcohol, opioids or nicotine.

Medications are also necessary for more severe and chronic mental health disorders, such as bipolar illness, recurrent major depression, psychotic disorders and certain anxiety disorders. You can provide information about medication-assisted treatment, and facilitate a medication evaluation for clients who want it or who you believe may benefit from combined treatments based on current problems and past experiences with treatment.

Some clients need help in overcoming their reluctance to consider medications either for an SUD or a psychiatric illness, so it may take time to persuade them to consider medications.

Alcohol Use Disorders

Medications for alcohol dependence include disulfiram (Antabuse®), naltrexone (oral form is Revia®, monthly injectable extended release form is Vivitrol®) or acamprosate (Campral®).

Disulfiram interrupts the metabolism of alcohol and creates an unpleasant and sometimes dangerous reaction if the client drinks with this drug in his system. Since this medicine can remain in the body for up to a week or more after the last dose the threat of an extremely unpleasant experience should he drink may influence the person not to drink while the medication in still in his system. By the time the medicine clears, the desire to drink may have lessened or stopped. *Naltrexone* occupies and blocks opioid mu receptor sites and thus decreases the pleasant effects of alcohol, often leading to reduced alcohol consumption simply because reinforcement is reduced or lacking altogether. *Acamprosate* improves the regulation of the neurotransmitters GABA and glutamate (associated with physiological craving) and is believed to decrease cravings for alcohol by normalizing these transmitters.

In addition to reducing cravings for alcohol, these medications may enhance motivation to stay sober, increase confidence in the ability to resist substance use and reduce the severity of lapses or relapses. A review by Garbutt and colleagues of 41 studies found that naltrexone and acamprosate were the most helpful pharmacologic adjuncts used with alcoholics. Clients taking naltrexone were much less likely to continue drinking following a slip compared to control subjects. O'Malley and colleagues found that alcoholic clients receiving RP along with naltrexone who returned to drinking were less likely to experience a relapse to heavy drinking compared to those who received supportive therapy plus naltrexone.

Opioid Use Disorders

Medications include methadone (Methadose®, Dolophine®) or buprenorphine (Subutex®; buprenorphine and naloxone combined is Suboxone®). Methadone, a full mu opioid receptor agonist, is taken in liquid or pill form and is dispensed only in licensed opiate treatment programs that are highly regulated. This "replacement" medicine helps to prevent withdrawal symptoms and reduce drug craving. The client may have to attend the clinic daily at first and then several days per week later. Buprenorphine is a partial mu opioid receptor agonist that addresses the biological basis of opioid dependence. Both Subutex® and Suboxone® are administered as a single film or tablet dose sublingually. Buprenorphine prevents opioid withdrawal symptoms by providing mild agonist effects and occupies opioid receptors so illicit opioids will have no effect. Suboxone is the preferred method of buprenorphine treatment because it deters clients from using the medication inappropriately or selling it illicitly. Buprenorphine is provided by specially trained physicians in private practice or as a part of a licensed SUDs treatment program. This drug is used to help detoxify the client or is used as a maintenance drug once sobriety has been stabilized. The opiate antagonist naltrexone (Revia® and Vivitrol®) is used to block the euphoric effects of opiate drugs, which can lead to an extinction of drug craving. Medication-assisted treatment should be used with therapy or counseling and/or participation in mutual support programs.

Tobacco Use Disorders

Medications include varenicline (Chantix®), buproprion SR (Zyban®), nicotine gum, nicotine lozenges, nasal spray, puffer ("inhaler") or transdermal patch. These may be used singly or in combination to help the client stop using nicotine and deal with strong cravings that often occur when a person stops using nicotine. Smoking cessation can also facilitate abstinence from alcohol and other drugs.

Stimulant Use Disorders

Many medications have been studied for stimulant (cocaine and methamphetamine) SUDs but at this time there are no FDA-approved medications for these SUDs. A vaccine to treat cocaine SUDs is also being studied to see if this helps cocaine addicts. Medications with limited efficacy used to treat stimulant use disorders include antidepressants, disulfiram, modafinil, topiramate, propranolol, buspirone, Lisdexamfetamine Dimesylate (brand name: Vyvanse) and baclofen.

Cannabis Use Disorders

Medications for marijuana dependence have not received a lot of attention. To date no medications have FDA approval for addiction to this drug.

Medications for Psychiatric Disorders

Medications are used for moderate to severe disorders, usually in combination with therapy or a psychosocial treatment program. Clinicians can help by educating clients about types and the uses of psychiatric medications, facilitating an evaluation by a physician, monitoring adherence if medications are used, and discussing the potential interaction between medications and alcohol use or other drug use. Following are medicines used for the major classifications of psychiatric disorders.

Mood Disorders

Drugs used to treat depression are called antidepressants. First-generation antidepressants include tricyclic antidepressants, for example:

- Amitriptyline (brand name Elavil)
- Nortriptlyine (brand name: Pamelor)
- Desipramine (brand name: Norpramin)
- Imipramine (brand name: Tofranil)

Another class of first-generation antidepressants are the monoamine oxidase (MAO) inhibitors such as:

- Phenelzine (brand name: Nardil)
- Selegiline (brand name: Parnate)

Second-generation antidepressants include selective serotonin reuptake inhibitors (SSRI) such as:

- Fluoxetine (brand name: Prozac)
- Sertraline (brand name: Zoloft)
- Citalopram (brand name: Celexa)
- Escitalopram (brand name: Lexapro)
- Paroxetine (brand name: Paxil)

Third-generation antidepressants include:

- Mirtazepine (brand name: Remeron)
- Venlafaxine and Venlafaxine XR (brand name: Effexor and Effexor XR)
- Duloxetine (brand name: Cymbalta)

New antidepressants include:

- Vortioxetine (brand name: Brintellix)
- Bupropion extended release (brand name: Forfivo XL)

Drugs to treat bipolar disorder include:

- Lithium carbonate, (brand name: Eskalith)
- Valproate (brand name: Depakote)
- Carbamazepine (brand name: Tegretol)
- Lamotrigine (brand name: Lamictal)
- Some antipsychotic medications are used as mood stabilizers in bipolar disorder, including risperidone, aripiprazole, and ziprasidone

Anxiety Disorders

Benzodiazepines produce their effects by binding to receptors in the limbic system and cerebral cortex in the brain. Some examples of benzodiazepines include:

- Diazepam (brand name: Valium)
- Clonazepam (brand name: Klonopin)
- Alprazolam (brand name: Xanax)

These medications have the potential for addiction, particularly in patients with substance use and alcohol use disorders. When taken in combination with alcohol or opiates, dangerous synergistic effects occur. Other antianxiety medications include buspirone (brand name: Buspar) and beta blockers; certain antidepressants are also first line treatment for anxiety disorders (SSRI, venlafaxine)

Psychotic Disorders

Medications for patients with schizophrenia and other psychotic disorders include first-generation, second-generation, and third-generation antipsychotic drugs. First-generation antipsychotics include:

- Haloperidol (brand name: Haldol)
- Chlorpromazine (brand name: Thorazine)

Second-generation antipsychotics include:

- Clozapine (brand name: Clozaril)
- Risperidone (brand name: Risperdal)
- Paliperidone (brand name: Invega)
- Olanzapine (brand name: Zyprexa)
- Ziprasidone (brand name: Geodon)
- Aripiprazole (brand name: Abilify)
- Iloperidone (brand name: Fanapt)
- Asenapine (brand name: Saphris)
- Lurasidone (brand name: Latuda)
- Quetiapine (brand name: Seroquel and Seroquel XR)

Some of these medications are also available in an injectable form

Attention Deficit Disorder

Some amphetamine-like stimulant drugs include methylphenidate (brand name: Ritalin; Sustained-release Ritalin, brand name: Concerta), dextroamphetamine (brand name: Adderall), non- stimulant medications include atomoxetine (brand name: Strattera).

Effects of Poor Adherence to Medications

Poor adherence to medications is a common problem and contributes to poor treatment outcome among individuals with medical disorders, psychiatric disorders, and SUDs. Poor adherence shows in failure to take medications as prescribed (taking too much or too little or missing doses), failure to renew prescriptions, and mixing medications with alcohol or illicit drugs. Clients may be poorly adherent to medications for a number of reasons:

- They are disorganized and have difficulty following a schedule of taking medicine.
- Their motivation to recover fluctuates.
- They have no access to care and they cannot afford to pay for medications.
- They experience uncomfortable side effects.
- They want to continue using alcohol or other drugs and do not want to risk interactions between these substances and medications

Monitor medication use and side effects to identify adherence problems early before these lead to adverse outcomes. This requires asking direct questions about medication use and side effects, and probing for specific details when there is some indication that medications are not being taken consistently as prescribed. For example, if a client attends an intensive outpatient program, part of the "check-in" procedure can include reporting on medication adherence (or non-adherence) in addition to reporting on substance use, or close calls, and attendance at support group meetings. Supervised administration of medications by either a family member or a concerned significant other could help enhance adherence to medications.

Managing a Substance Use or Related Addictive Disorder

Craving Recognition and Management

Cravings, urges or desires to use substances are common when a person stops using alcohol or other drugs. These are triggered by environmental cues associated with prior use such as the sight or smell of the substance or something associated with using it (e.g., a specific person, location, event, object, song). Or, they are triggered by internal factors such as emotions or thoughts. For example, some clients report increased cravings in response to feeling bored or anxious. Others report increased cravings when they start believing that they need some "action" to make life fun or want to escape from the monotony of life.

Dr. Nora Volkow, the director of the National Institute on Drug Abuse, hypothesizes that the dopamine stimulation that occurs with long term drug use leads to disruption of the brain circuitry involved in regulating drives. This in turn leads to a conditioned response, such as craving when exposed to external stimuli, which may lead to relapse to compulsive drug taking. And, since there are so many external stimuli associated with SUDs, cravings are common and can come out of the blue when not expected.

You can provide information about cues and how they trigger cravings for alcohol or other drugs. Teach clients how to monitor and record cravings (in early recovery), associated thoughts and behavioral outcomes in a daily log or journal. This can help them become more vigilant and prepared to cope with cravings. And, they may identify patterns to their cravings and how they respond to them.

Cognitive interventions include changing thoughts about the craving, urge or desire to use, challenging euphoric recall (how good it felt being high), talking oneself through the craving, thinking beyond the high by identifying negative consequences of using again (immediate and delayed), positive benefits of not using, using recovery slogans and delaying the decision to use.

Behavioral interventions include avoiding, leaving a situation or event, changing situations that trigger or worsen a craving, redirecting activities, getting involved in pleasant activities, getting help or support from others by admitting and talking about cravings, and hearing how others have survived them or attending self-help support group meetings.

Taking medications such as disulfiram, naltrexone or acamprosate may reduce cravings and increase confidence in the ability to cope with desires for alcohol, opioids or nicotine. Combining medications with counseling gives the maximum benefit in dealing with cravings.

Marlatt describes an interesting experiential strategy for managing cravings. The client is instructed to "detach" from his craving by externalizing and labeling it. Similar to a surfer who must learn to ride the waves so as not to get wiped out, the addicted client imagines riding "the crest of an urge or craving, maintaining balance until the crest has finally broken, and the wave of feeling subsides." Another strategy is using "mastery imagery" to help the client view herself as successfully defeating the craving, for example, by driving a large tank and crushing the craving.

The figure that follows illustrates one way to think about cravings and how to manage them. It shows that many factors precipitate cravings, which can manifest in many different ways. Cravings or urges affect thinking, feelings and behaviors, which then leads to a decision on whether or not to use an active coping strategy. Since cravings are so common and can be quite intense, clients need a variety of coping strategies to call upon when they desire alcohol or other drugs.

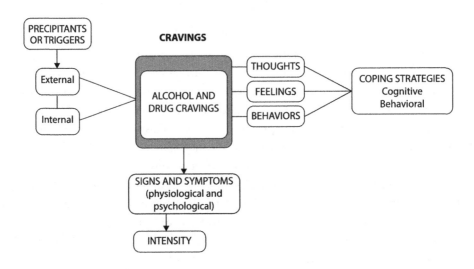

Evaluate Environmental Triggers or Cues

While many triggers and cues are outside of the client's control, not all are. In early recovery, for example, clients can be advised to avoid high-risk people, places, things and events that are associated with substance use. The idea is to minimize exposure to people or situations that increase the risk of relapse. The more obvious ones are active substance abusers, bars, clubs, parties and places or events where drugs are used. Avoidance is usually recommended, because it takes away the direct threat often felt, especially during early recovery, when the recovering person is less experienced using active coping strategies to manage cravings.

Clients can also take active steps to modify their immediate environment. The most obvious examples are to remove alcohol, drugs and drug paraphernalia such as needles, pipes or other items associated with preparing or using drugs or partying.

Following are examples of both internal and external triggers common among individuals in recovery:

Client Examples of Internal and External Triggers	
Internal	**External**
"I am so bored with recovery. I need some action."	"My girlfriend smoked dope in front of me."
"I'm pissed at my boss; it makes me want to drink."	"Everyone drinks at family gatherings. I want to fit in and feel normal!"
"I'm real upset with my husband."	"Hearing certain music makes me want to get high. It reminds me of partying."
"I can't get the idea of drugs out of my head. I want to get high real bad."	"Seeing baby powder reminded me of cocaine."
"I wonder if I am capable of coping with problems and staying sober."	"Feeling a needle for a flu shot reminded me of dope."
"Why would a few drinks hurt?"	"I found a joint in my sweater drawer. It looks so tempting."
"This pain is too much. A joint would make me feel better."	"My boyfriend wants us to use cocaine for better sex."

Identify and Prepare to Resist Social Pressures to Use Substances

Direct and indirect social pressures often lead to increased thoughts and desires around using substances as well as anxiety regarding his or her ability to refuse offers to drink alcohol or use other drugs. In some instances, the client can be taken by surprise at the strength of such pressures, especially when they are unexpected. For example, a heroin-addicted woman who had been drug-free for several months received an unplanned visit from an old friend with whom she used to get high. After the client invited the friend into her house, the friend casually asked if she wanted to get high on crack. The client said she did not want to. The friend then asked the client if it was OK to smoke crack in her house. The client reluctantly gave in to this request and later in the evening ended up smoking crack. The next day she reflected on this experience and felt guilty for using drugs. However, she then told herself if she was going to relapse it might as well be on her drug of choice, so she called her dealer and bought heroin. In reviewing this experience with her clinician, the client realized that she was not fully prepared to refuse social pressures to use drugs and, she had made two "apparently irrelevant decisions" that impacted on her relapse (first, by letting her drug using friend come into her home, and second, by letting this friend smoke crack cocaine in front of her).

You can help your client identify high-risk relationships (e.g., living or socializing with, or dating an active substance abuser) and social situations or events in which the client may be exposed to, or offered, substances. The next step is to assess the effects of these social pressures on the thoughts, feelings and behaviors of the client. Planning, practicing, and implementing coping strategies is the next step. Coping strategies include avoidance of high-risk people, situations and events when appropriate, and the use of verbal, cognitive, or behavioral skills. Rehearsing ways to refuse offers of drugs or alcohol is one practical and easy-to-use intervention. The final step of this process involves teaching the client to evaluate the results of a given coping strategy and to modify it as needed. Ineffective strategies need to be replaced and effective ones continued.

While some social situations cannot be avoided, it is not unusual for a client to sabotage recovery by making what Marlatt refers to as "apparently-irrelevant-decisions," which are a "set-up" for relapse. For example, a recovering drug-addicted client accepted a date with a man she knew was still using drugs and put herself in a very risky situation. An alcoholic sober for several months went on a weekend golfing trip with several friends with whom he used to drink. Since these weekend trips often involved excessive drinking, just by accepting this invitation he put himself at higher risk for relapse to alcohol use. Although both of these individuals successfully resisted pressures to use substances, they reported feeling extremely awkward, anxious and "close" to using. It is likely that similar situations have occurred with others and contributed to their relapses.

In some cases, pressures to use alcohol or other drugs result from relationships with active substance abusers or being part of a high-risk social network in which substance use plays a significant role. Therefore, the client needs to assess his/her social network and if needed, learn ways to limit or end relationships that represent a high risk for relapse.

The chart that follows illustrates the different types of social pressures (direct and indirect), which lead to different effects on the person in recovery. As with other issues in recovery, multiple coping strategies are needed to successfully cope with social pressure to use alcohol or other drugs.

SOCIAL PRESSURES

Identify and Manage Inaccurate Thinking ("stinking thinking")

Errors in thinking (also called cognitive distortions) are associated with both psychiatric and substance use disorders, and have been implicated in relapse to either type of disorder. Marlatt believes that cognitive distortions may increase the probability that an initial slip or lapse will develop into a total relapse for the client. Twelve-Step programs refer to these patterns of thinking as "stinking thinking" and suggest that recovering people need to alter their thinking if they are to remain alcohol- and drug-free.

Teaching clients to identify their inaccurate or negative thinking patterns or cognitive errors (e.g., black-and-white thinking, awfulizing, overgeneralizing, catastrophizing, jumping to conclusions, etc.) and evaluate how these affect recovery and relapse is one strategy. Clients can then be taught to use counter-thoughts to challenge their thinking errors or specific negative thoughts.

One way to achieve this is to have the client discuss or write down:

- Specific relapse-related thoughts (e.g., "Relapse can't happen to me," "I'll never use alcohol or other drugs again," "I can't control my use of alcohol or other drugs," "A few drinks, tokes, pills, lines won't hurt," "Recovery isn't happening fast enough," "I need alcohol or other drugs to have fun," and "my problem is cured.").
- What is wrong with such thinking in terms of potential impact on relapse.
- New self-statements or thoughts that counteract negative thinking. Many of the AA and NA slogans were devised to help alcoholics and drug addicted individuals alter their thinking and survive desires to use substances. Slogans such as "this too will pass," "let go and let God," and "one day at a time" can help the client manage thoughts of using.

Increase Healthy Leisure Activities

Clients sometimes struggle when they get sober and get easily bored, or they do not have healthy leisure interests to bring them enjoyment. One strategy is to help clients rediscover enjoyable activities that did not evolve around substance use that they enjoyed in the past but stopped as their SUD progressed.

Another strategy is to help clients identify and engage in new activities. What is important is engaging in activities that bring pleasure and enjoyment, help the client stay connected to others, and give the client a sense of meaning or involvement in life. This is difficult for some clients who report they "need action" and have trouble enjoying the simple pleasures in life.

Identify and Manage Decrease in Motivation

Motivation to change and follow a recovery plan can change quickly, especially in early recovery. This is a common challenge for those with substance use, psychiatric or co-occurring disorders. Clients with SUDs often enter treatment as a result of external motivation, which shows in pressure to engage in treatment from the legal system, the family or an employer. A client can be highly motivated to change some areas of life, and less motivated to change others.

Factors impacting on motivation include severity of symptoms and illness, emotions, thinking, coping strategies, impulsivity, support from others and past experiences in recovery. Two interventions aimed at enhancing motivation to change include motivational interviewing (MI) and motivational incentives (MotInc). MI has been used with clients with substance use, psychiatric, co-occurring and/or medical problems. MotInc is used mainly in programs that treat SUDs.

Monitoring motivation on a daily basis in the early months of recovery is one helpful strategy. The client can rate motivation to change an addictive behavior (e.g., alcohol, tobacco or other drug use) or other behavior (following a diet or exercise plan, challenging anxious or depressed thinking) on a scale of 1–10 (1=low motivation to change; 5=moderate motivation to change; 10=high motivation to change). The client establishes an acceptable range of motivation, and devises a plan should motivation dip below this range. The biggest challenge is managing periods of low motivation.

Another strategy is to use a "decision matrix" in which the client identifies positive and negative aspects of change, both short-term and long-term. The client fights through a period of low motivation when long-term benefits of change are identified.

Use a Daily Inventory

A daily inventory keeps the client vigilant about recovery and focused on recovering one day at a time. Such an inventory can be used at the beginning of the day to identify issues to work on during the day, and to identify recovery strategies to use. It can also be used at the end of the day to reflect on the day. Some questions for the day end inventory include:

- What problems or goals did I work on today?
- What progress did I make and how satisfied am I with my progress?
- Were there any relapse warning signs present today that represent a potential threat to my ongoing recovery?
- If yes, what steps can I take to manage my problems or relapse warning signs to reduce my risk of an actual relapse?

PSYCHIATRIC ILLNESS MANAGEMENT SKILLS

Illness management skills refers to a broad set of strategies designed to help clients with serious mental illness collaborate with healthcare professionals, learn how to cope with the symptoms of their disorder(s) and reduce their risk of relapse or recurrence. Recovery occurs when people use their strengths and abilities to pursue recovery or personal goals. Research on illness management for persons with severe mental illness, including 40 randomized controlled studies, indicates that: 1) psychoeducation improves people's knowledge of mental illness; 2) behavioral tailoring helps people take medication as prescribed; 3) RP programs reduce symptoms, relapses and rehospitalizations; and 4) coping skills training using cognitive-behavioral techniques reduces the severity and distress of persistent symptoms.

MONITOR ACUTE SYMPTOMS OF A PSYCHIATRIC DISORDER

You can teach your client to regularly review or monitor the major symptoms of his specific psychiatric disorder (s). These may include mood, psychotic, somatic or behavioral symptoms.

Symptom monitoring helps clinician and client determine if improvements are being made. This also helps them know if symptoms are worsening and may require a new treatment strategy. For example, a client with moderate depression may elect to participate in psychotherapy and try to recover without medication. If mood symptoms do not improve or worsen with therapy alone, the clinician may then persuade the client to consider a trial of medications and arrange an evaluation with a psychiatrist or other prescriber.

When symptoms of an acute episode of illness significantly improve or remit, regular monitoring enables the client and clinician to identify early signs of relapse. This can reduce the possibility of relapse to a full episode of illness.

Managing Persistent Symptoms of Chronic Disorders

Recurrent depression, bipolar illness, schizophrenia, and many of the anxiety and personality disorders are chronic conditions in which some symptoms may never totally remit. For example, individuals with schizophrenia may hallucinate or have delusions despite taking antipsychotic medications. Clients with depressive or anxiety disorders may still experience symptoms despite being treated with medications, therapy or combined treatments.

Dr. Alan Belleck and colleagues and Dr. Robert Liberman developed social skills training programs for clients with chronic mental disorders such as schizophrenia. One of the treatment modules in Dr. Liberman's program teaches clients four main skills to manage symptoms and reduce the risk of psychiatric relapse:

- Identify early signs of psychotic relapse.
- Manage early signs of psychotic relapse so the client's condition does not worsen.
- Manage persistent symptoms of illness.
- Avoid alcohol and drugs since these substances interfere with the efficacy of medications or the client's motivation to recover.

One of the strategies used to manage persistent symptoms is to have the client identify and label (or name) his persistent symptom(s). For example, a "hallucination" could be labeled or named by the client as a hallucination, hearing voices, or hearing voices telling the client that he is worthless. The client then rates the persistent symptom on a daily basis. Once an acceptable baseline is determined, the client and clinician can agree upon a symptom rating that indicates action is needed. Strategies to manage persistent symptoms are taught to the client so he has ideas on how to manage these should they occur.

Monitor Participation in Treatment and Recovery

Treatment participation can be monitored by discussing adherence to taking medications, attending therapy sessions, attending group sessions in a partial hospital program or intensive outpatient program, or completing therapeutic assignments aimed at helping the client reach goals. The clinician can also engage the client in a review of the treatment experience to identify and address impasses in therapy as well as client behaviors that could sabotage progress in treatment. For example, if a client fails to make agreed upon behavioral changes yet constantly demands changes in medications when symptoms change, the clinician can explore this in sessions. A joint session with the psychiatrist can also help in such a situation since clients can sometimes convince doctors to change medications without giving them all of the information that was provided to a clinician.

Monitoring participation in recovery support groups such as AA, NA, DRA (Dual Recovery Anonymous) or mental health related groups can help the client spot problems early, which in turn can have an impact on reducing relapse risk. It is not unusual, for example, for a client's relapse warning signs to show in reducing or stopping recovery activities without first discussing such changes with his therapist. Such monitoring also gives the therapist an idea on whether the client is an "active" or "passive" participant in support programs. Those who actively participate in these programs usually do better than those who are passive and do not actively use the "tools" of the program.

EMOTION MANAGEMENT SKILLS

Difficulty managing emotions or moods is common with substance use, psychiatric and co-occurring disorders. Inability to manage emotions or moods can contribute to relapse with any type of disorder or impact on the quality of life of the client. Addressing emotion management issues is a key component of recovery for many clients. Following is a discussion of interventions to help clients learn or improve their emotion management skills.

Help Client Identify and Manage Emotions

In our treatment programs we often implement quality improvement projects in which we ask clients about their experiences and ideas related to their treatment and recovery. One project involved asking 168 clients from 14 different treatment groups in residential and ambulatory programs to state what they thought were the challenges they faced in recovery from their SUDs. The category with the most responses was "dealing with emotions." In order of concern for clients was dealing with painful feelings, boredom, anxiety and fear, depression, guilt and shame, anger, hopelessness, emptiness, and loneliness.

Another project had over 100 clients complete a questionnaire to identify how many had symptoms of "social anxiety" and how many "avoided" social situations because of this anxiety. About one-third of our clients identified significant social anxiety and most of these avoided situations causing this anxiety. This is something clients seldom talk about in treatment if clinicians do not ask about it. And, this issue has great implications for recovery since many of these clients will not attend, or will drop out early from mutual support groups due to their excessive anxiety.

Most clinicians know that emotions and feelings are factors in a substantial number of relapses. The acronym "HALT," cited by AA and NA members speaks to this important issue of negative emotions (i.e., "don't get too Hungry, Angry, Lonely, or Tired").

Interventions for helping clients develop coping skills for managing negative emotional states depend on the issues and needs of the individual. For example, strategies for dealing with depression that accompanies the realization that SUDs caused havoc in one's life may vary from those for dealing with depression that is part of a bipolar or major depressive illness. Interventions to help the client who occasionally gets angry and seeks solace in substances may vary from those needed to help the client who is chronically angry. The former may need help in expressing anger appropriately rather than suppressing it. The chronically angry client may need to learn how to contain angry feelings, since these are often expressed impulsively and inappropriately. This type of client can benefit from cognitive techniques that help challenge and change angry thoughts. The chronically angry person may also benefit from seeing his or her angry disposition as a "character defect." Psychotherapy and/or use of the Twelve-Step program of AA and NA may help the client modify behaviors associated with this trait.

Interventions for clients who report feelings of chronic boredom, emptiness, or joylessness similarly depend on the specific nature of the emotional state. One client may need help in learning how to use free time or how to have fun without substances. Another may need help in developing new relationships or finding new activities that provide a sense of meaning in life and an emotional connection to other people. The client may also need to alter beliefs regarding fun, excitement, and what is important in life. Many addicted individuals report that being drug-free is boring compared with the high provided by the drug or behaviors associated with getting the drug or "living on the edge." In such a case, the client needs not only to change behaviors but beliefs as well.

In addition, problems managing anger are common among clients with personality disorders. For example, many women with borderline personality disorders internalize their anger and hurt themselves by cutting or burning their flesh or overeating. Men with borderline or antisocial personality disorders often externalize their anger and lash out at others verbally or physically. These or other psychiatric disorders may require treatment for the client to be able to recover from the SUDs.

Increase Gratitude and Positive Emotions or Experiences

In recent years the positive psychology movement has focused on the importance of positive emotions such as gratitude, love, forgiveness, kindness, altruism and many others. Studies show that individuals who increase their expression of gratitude and other positive emotions improve their emotional health and well-being. Therefore, educating clients and helping them incorporate strategies in daily life to increase their positive emotions can enhance their recovery as well as improve the quality of their lives. Many investigators of the impact of positive emotions have published books for individuals interested in understanding and increasing positive emotions in their lives.

Facilitate an Evaluation and Treatment of Mood or Anxiety Disorders

Some clients with problems managing their moods or feelings may have a psychiatric disorder that needs to be evaluated and treated. For example, there are high rates of depression, bipolar and anxiety disorders among clients with SUDs. Many with anxiety disorders have significant depression, and many with depression have significant anxiety. Problems with their moods may be a result of a psychiatric illness rather than any effects of SUDs or the problems caused by it.

RELATIONSHIPS AND COMMUNICATION SKILLS

Many of the therapies for substance use or psychiatric disorders focus on interpersonal relationships and communication skills such as more direct, open and assertive communication among family members.

Improve Communication Skills

Many researchers and clinicians address RP from a broader perspective that includes focus on interpersonal relationships and support systems. The *Coping Skills* model of Monti and colleagues includes considerable focus on interpersonal skills such as giving and receiving criticism, refusing offers for alcohol, refusing requests, developing close and intimate relationships and enhancing social support networks. McGrady has modified Marlatt's cognitive-behavioral model of RP and applied it to couples in recovery. O'Farrell and colleagues developed an RP protocol for use in combination with behavioral marital therapy. Maisto and colleagues found that alcoholics who were treated with their spouses with RP in addition to marital therapy had shorter and less severe relapses than clients not receiving RP.

Positive family and social supports generally enhance recovery. Families are more likely to support the recovery of the addicted member if they are engaged in treatment and have an opportunity to ask questions, share their concerns and experiences, learn practical coping strategies and learn behaviors to avoid. This is more likely to occur if the member with the substance use disorder understands the impact of substance abuse on the family and makes amends for some of the adverse effects on the family.

Many of the family interventions for psychiatric illness promote the importance of positive communication. This may show in reducing hostile or negative comments or interactions and increasing positive expression of feelings or support towards the client.

Impact of Illness on the Family

Family members are often adversely affected by a loved one's disorder(s). Any substance use or psychiatric disorder or combination of disorders can impact on the family system and individual members in many ways. Family communication, cohesion and mood may suffer. Individual members are at increased risk of feeling a burden and thus feeling anxious, worried, angry, depressed or overwhelmed. Children of parents with a substance use or psychiatric disorder are at increased risk of these disorders as well as other potential problems in life (school, relationships, health). Examining the impact of one's illnesses on the family can initially raise anxiety and feelings of guilt. However, over time, as recovery progresses, the client and family may work towards closer, healthier relationships. Some clients may want to avoid or minimize talking about the impact of their disorders on their families. These clients may need to be reassured that the family may also heal as recovery progresses and their experiences are shared and heard by others including the client.

Family Involvement in Treatment

Families have many questions and concerns, and need information to help them better understand these disorders and recovery. Involving them in treatment helps them to learn what they can and cannot do to help support the family member with the substance use or psychiatric or co-occurring disorders. Involvement can also help the family member become aware of relapse warning signs and how to point these out to their loved one prior to an actual relapse occurring.

Participation in treatment sessions may help the family deal with their own feelings and reactions to the member with the disorder(s). A family member can contribute to a loved one's relapse either purposely or inadvertently. Calls to invite family members to sessions are often needed to engage them in the treatment process.

Family Involvement in Recovery

Families may also benefit from participation in mutual support programs such as Al-Anon or Nar-Anon or NAMI (National Alliance of the Mentally Ill). Involvement in support programs can help families understand their loved one's disorder(s), learn to work on their own issues, which in turn can have a positive impact on the addicted member's recovery. Other families can provide education, support and helpful ideas on coping with the many challenges that families face when a loved one has a substance use, psychiatric or co-occurring disorder.

MUTUAL SUPPORT PROGRAMS (MSPs)

Clients can be oriented and prepared to get actively involved in support groups such as AA, NA and DRA. Active involvement refers to attending meetings, getting and using a sponsor, and using the "tools" of the program.

Help them to develop a network of support to make their recovery a "we" process. Sponsors, other recovering peers in mutual support programs, supportive friends and family members may become part of an individual's support network.

Following are some suggested steps for helping clients develop a support network. First, the client needs to identify whom to involve in or exclude from this network. Others who abuse substances, harbor strong negative feelings toward the recovering person, or who are not supportive of recovery should be excluded. The client can then determine how and when to ask for support. Behavioral rehearsal can help the client practice ways to make specific requests for support. Rehearsal also helps increase confidence as well as clarify thoughts and feelings regarding reaching out for help. Some clients feel guilty or ashamed and question whether they deserve support from others. Others have such strong pride that the thought of asking others for support is difficult to accept. Rehearsal may clarify the client's ambivalence regarding asking for help or support from others. This process also helps the client better understand how the person being asked for support may respond, thus preparing the client for potentially negative responses from others.

Some clients find it helpful to put their action plan in writing. This plan can address the following issues:

- How to communicate about and deal with relapse warning signs and high-risk situations.
- How to interrupt a lapse.
- How to intervene if a relapse occurs.
- The importance of exploring all the details of a lapse/relapse after the client is stable so that it can be used as a learning experience.

A plan can make both the recovering person and family feel more in control when and if faced with the possibility of a relapse. This helps everyone take a proactive approach to recovery rather than sitting back passively and waiting for problems to worsen.

RELAPSE RECOGNITION AND INTERRUPTION SKILLS

Identify and Manage High Risk Relapse Factors

The need to recognize and manage high-risk (HR) factors is an essential component of RP. A framework that we have used in groups and included in a written workbook adapts Marlatt's categories of high risk situations into the following:

Upsetting feelings or difficulty managing emotions: anger, anxiety, boredom, depression, guilt or shame.

Social situations and pressures to use alcohol or drugs: difficulty saying no, having a partner, spouse or roommate who uses substances at home.

Sobriety plan or treatment-related problems: change in motivation to stay sober, missing or dropping out of treatment or mutual support programs.

Relationship problems: serious problems with spouse or partner, hard to enjoy sex without being high.

Urges, cravings, temptations or testing your control: being around others using, having drugs or alcohol at home, seeing or smelling alcohol or drugs.

Other high-risk situations: not taking medications as prescribed, other addictions (gambling, sex), psychiatric problems.

HR factors involve intrapersonal and interpersonal situations in which the client feels vulnerable to substance use. *Relapse is more likely to occur as a result of lack of coping skills than the high risk situation itself* so the clinician should assess the client's coping style to determine targets for clinical intervention.

The meaning of specific HR factors also varies among clients. RP strategies and interventions will therefore need to take into account the nuances of each client's HR factors. For example, two clients identified depression as a serious relapse risk. In the first case, depression was described as the rather common and normal feeling experienced when the client realized that his drug SUDs caused serious problems in his relationships with his wife and children. Getting his family involved in his treatment, facilitating their attendance at Nar-Anon meetings, making amends to them, and spending time with them led to improvement in his mood. In the second case, the client's depression worsened significantly the longer she was sober from alcohol. While she felt some of the behavioral and cognitive strategies explored in therapy were helpful in improving her mood, it wasn't until she took an antidepressant that she experienced the full benefits of treatment. Both of these clients reported that an improved mood was a significant factor in their ability to prevent a subsequent relapse to their SUDs.

For some clients, identifying high-risk factors and developing new coping strategies for each are inadequate, since they may identify many risk factors. Such clients need help in taking a more global approach to recovery and may need to learn specific problem-solving skills. Marlatt, for example, suggests that in addition to teaching clients "specific" RP skills to deal with high-risk factors, the clinician should also utilize "global" approaches such as problem solving or skill training strategies (e.g., behavioral rehearsal, covert modeling, assertiveness training), cognitive reframing (e.g., coping imagery, reframing reactions to lapse/relapse), and lifestyle interventions (e.g., meditation, exercise, relaxation).

The following chart illustrates one way to think about high risk factors. Help the client identify these factors and the specific details, identify (and practice) then implement coping strategies, evaluate results, and change coping strategies as needed. These steps focus on "action."

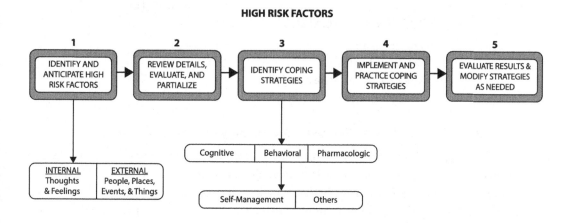

HIGH RISK FACTORS

Identify and Manage Relapse Warning Signs of SUDs

Clients are better prepared for the challenges of recovery if they understand that clues or warning signs often precede an actual lapse or relapse. Although a relapse may result from an impulsive act, attitudinal, emotional, cognitive, and/or behavioral changes may show days, weeks or even longer prior to the actual ingestion of substances (see chart on next page). An individual's clues or warning signs can be conceptualized as links in a relapse chain.

Warning signs may be overt and obvious, such as a significant increase in substance cravings, or stopping or reducing treatment sessions or self-help meetings without discussing this decision first with a therapist or sponsor. Warning signs can also be overt and more idiosyncratic or unique to the client. For example, a drug addicted client reported that one of his main warning signs was the return of dishonest behaviors. His review of several relapses helped him discover that even before obvious signs of relapse were present, he would start becoming dishonest by lying, scamming others and stealing money from his employer. Shortly thereafter, the more obvious relapse warning signs occurred such as thoughts of needing some action, contacting old friends who were still using drugs, dropping out of treatment, and reducing contact with his NA friends and sponsor.

Clients in treatment for the first time can benefit from reviewing common relapse warning signs identified by others in recovery. The clinician can ask the client to review the relapse experience in detail to learn the connections between thoughts, feelings, events or situations, and relapse to substance use. My (DD) survey of 511 clients found that "Understanding the Relapse Process" was the topic rated as most useful by clients participating in a residential treatment program.

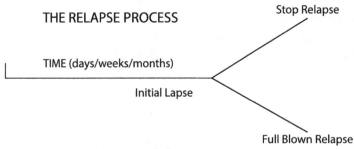

THE RELAPSE PROCESS

Stop Relapse

TIME (days/weeks/months)

Initial Lapse

Full Blown Relapse

RELAPSE WARNING SIGNS

• Attitude changes
• Behavior changes
• Mood/emotional state changes
• Thought changes

Identify and Manage Relapse Warning Signs of Psychiatric Illness

Early warning signs following a remission of psychiatric illness may show in a return of some symptoms. Or, warning signs may show in a worsening of symptoms that never fully remitted. Similar to SUDs, changes in thinking, emotions and behaviors can also indicate the potential return of a psychiatric illness. Some examples include: 1) a client with schizophrenia shows a deterioration in personal hygiene; 2) a client with depression sleeps longer; or 3) a client with any type of psychiatric disorder thinks about or actually cuts down or stops attending scheduled sessions with a psychiatrist or therapist.

Prepare to Manage Setbacks (Lapse, Relapse, Recurrence)

Clients should have an emergency plan to follow if they lapse so that a full-blown relapse can be avoided. However, if a full-blown relapse occurs, the client also needs to have strategies to interrupt it. The specific intervention strategies should be based on the severity of the client's lapse or relapse, coping mechanisms, and prior history of relapse. Helpful interventions include using self-talk or behavioral procedures to stop a lapse or relapse; asking family, AA or NA sponsors, friends, or professionals for help; carrying an *emergency card* with names and phone numbers of others who can be called upon for support; or carrying a *reminder card* that gives specific instructions on what to do if a lapse or relapse occurs. Marlatt recommends developing a relapse contract with clients that outlines specific steps to take in the event of a future relapse. The aim of this contract is to formalize or reinforce the client's commitment to change. He also recommends teaching clients strategies to manage a lapse such as:

- Stop, look and listen
- Keep calm
- Renew your commitment
- Review the situation leading up to the lapse
- Make an immediate plan for recovery
- Ask for help

Once a relapsed client is stable, analyzing lapses or relapses is a valuable process that can aid recovery. The client can identify warning signs preceding actual substance use as well as the high risk factors that may have played a role in the relapse. This process can help the client reframe a "failure" as a "learning" experience and prepare for future high-risk situations. It can also help the client determine if any irrelevant decisions were made that impacted on relapse.

Have an Emergency Plan for Suicidality

Suicide is the tenth leading cause of death in the U.S., and the second leading cause among young people between the ages of 15 and 29. While women have higher rates of suicidal ideation and plans, and make more attempts, men have much higher rates of completion of suicide due to lethal methods used.

According to experts, over 80% of attempters and nearly all completers have a psychiatric disorder. Most are depressed. Substance use is another risk factor that increases the risk of suicide as the effects of alcohol or drugs can affect judgment and decision making. Other risk factors include recent loss (relationship, job, other), suicide by significant other, a prior attempt and current plan, a history of self-harm behaviors, lack of support and inability to accept help from others.

The best protection against suicide is being involved in treatment that improves the psychiatric condition. Other protective factors include feeling connected to others, involving the family in treatment, using problem solving skills, religious beliefs that support a desire to live, lack of access to weapons or lethal means to kills oneself, and having a purpose in life.

A clinician can make an agreement with the client regarding steps that he or the family will take if he feels suicidal or has a plan. This may involve open discussions with the client, scheduling emergency sessions with the therapist and/or psychiatrist, seeking help at a crisis center or via phone on a crisis hotline, or going to a psychiatric emergency room to get evaluated for hospital admission.

LIFESTYLE CHANGES

In addition to identifying and managing intrapersonal and interpersonal high-risk relapse factors, clients benefit from global changes to restore or achieve a balance in their lives. Development of a healthy lifestyle is important in reducing stress that makes the client more vulnerable to relapse. Lifestyle can be assessed by evaluating patterns of daily activities, sources of stress, stressful life events, daily hassles and uplifts, balance between wants (activities engaged in for pleasure or self-fulfillment) and shoulds (external demands), health, exercise and relaxation patterns, interpersonal activities, and religious beliefs.

Helping clients develop positive habits or substitute indulgences (e.g., jogging, meditation, relaxation, exercise, hobbies or creative tasks, etc.) for substance use can help to balance their lifestyles. Clients with a need for greater adventure or action may get involved in more active and challenging activities.

Teach Mindfulness Skills

In recent years, mindfulness has been incorporated into treatment for psychiatric disorders and RP practices for SUDs (called mindfulness-based relapse prevention or MBRP). MBRP integrates RP and mindfulness meditation practices as a way of helping clients learn skills to make behavior changes. This approach helps clients understand the changing nature of their minds, bodies and environments so they can better cope with cravings or urges for substances or the other challenges of recovery. In a recent study by Bowen and colleagues, MBRP showed promise as an aftercare treatment for those completing a residential program for a SUD. It involved eight weekly group sessions that focused on:

Automatic pilot and relapse: This helps the client become more aware of actions and unconscious thinking as these relate to alcohol or drug use.

Awareness of triggers and cravings: The client learns to accept cravings without automatically reacting so that there is an increase in choices in how to respond to a craving.

Mindfulness in daily life: The client learns meditation and how to accept physical sensations and emotions without reacting in harmful ways.

Mindfulness in high-risk situations: The client identifies personal high risk factors and ways to cope with feelings that these generate without using substances.

Acceptance and skillful action: The client learns to accept unwanted thoughts, feelings and sensations, and to take skillful actions to cope with high risk situations in daily life.

Seeing thoughts as thoughts: The client learns how thoughts affect the relapse cycle and how to work with problematic thoughts.

Self-care and lifestyle balance: The client learns to respond to personal warning signs and the importance of having nourishing activities as part of a healthy life.

Social support and continuing practice: Skills learned in the program are reviewed and the importance of building a support system is emphasized. Plans to use mindfulness practices in daily life are shared among group members.

Mindfulness-based stress reduction (MBSR) is a structured group program that employs mindfulness meditation to alleviate suffering associated with physical, psychosomatic and psychiatric disorders including depression and anxiety. The program is based upon a systematic procedure to develop enhanced awareness of moment-to-moment experience of perceptible mental processes. The approach assumes that greater awareness will reduce negative affect and improve coping.

The techniques of mindfulness include meditation, with their emphasis on developing detached observation and awareness of the contents of consciousness, may represent a powerful cognitive behavioral coping strategy for transforming the ways in which individuals respond to life events. They may also have potential for relapse prevention in mood and anxiety disorders.

Address "Other" SUDs and
Problems that Interfere with Recovery

Many clients have other SUDs or co-existing medical, psychiatric, vocational, occupational, legal, housing, family, social or other problems, which can impact on recovery or relapse. Referrals may be needed for case management, social service agencies, medical or psychiatric services, other mutual support programs (e.g., GA, SA, SLA), or other SUDs treatment programs to address these other problems or SUDs.

CHAPTER 4

Counseling Aids for Relapse Prevention

This chapter reviews clinical aids to use with clients or their families. These aids are listed alphabetically for ease of reference. Counseling aids include techniques for counseling sessions plus reading and writing tasks assigned to clients. Many of the counseling aids, such as the "Relapse Fantasy" or the "Relapse Prevention Workbooks" can be adapted to individual or group counseling. You can assign clients "homework" tasks between individual or group counseling sessions.

ADDICT AFTERCARE: RECOVERY TRAINING AND SELF-HELP

The *Addict Aftercare Model* described in Chapter Two has a manual consisting of 23 "recovery training" sessions and related handouts for clients. Each session is organized according to objectives, background information about the topic, materials needed, key points, and format. Each session relates to recovery and falls in one of these four general topics:

Being Clean: cravings, dangerous situations, social pressures, pain, and slips.

Highs and Lows: having fun without drugs, dealing with stress, prescription medications.

Social Relationships: making new friends, love and intimate relationships, family issues, community service.

Work and Growth: presenting past employment history, job problems, planning ahead.

CHALLENGING THOUGHTS OF USING SUBSTANCES

Accord to both Marlatt and Daley, negative, inaccurate or "relapse-related" thoughts and "cognitive distortions" are associated with relapse. AA and NA use the term "stinking thinking" to refer to these. "Challenging relapse thoughts" helps the client: 1) become aware of common relapse-related thoughts of others with a SUD; 2) identify personal relapse thoughts, evaluate what is faulty about them, or thinking pattern; and 3) practice challenging the thought(s) to cope positively and stay sober.

Seven common relapse-related thoughts to make clients more aware of cognitive aspects of the relapse process and practice counter statements are:

- Relapse can't happen to me
- I'll 'never' use alcohol or drugs again
- I can 'control' my use of alcohol or other drugs

51

- A few drinks, tokes, pills, lines, won't hurt
- Recovery isn't happening fast enough
- I 'need' alcohol or other drugs to have fun
- My problem is 'cured.'

Clients can also add their own thoughts to this list to make it more applicable to them.

The process is simple. The client reviews the list of the seven thoughts above, then writes down what is wrong with each one followed by one or more counterstatements. The same process can be used with personalized thoughts identified by the client. The main skill taught is to identify and challenge thinking that can lead to relapse.

COGNITIVE DISTORTIONS AND PSYCHIATRIC RELAPSE

Experts in the cognitive treatment of depression, such as Drs. Aaron Beck and David Burns, have written about "depressogenic assumptions" and how these impact on depression. These assumptions or "cognitive distortions" are found among addicted clients as well and may contribute to the relapse process.

Clinicians can teach clients about these cognitive distortions, relate them to their individual life situations, and develop coping strategies to challenge them. These cognitive distortions, adapted to the relapse process, are:

Black and white or dichotomous thinking is seeing things as either one extreme or the other, and not in terms of "degrees." The person either thinks he is doing well or poorly in recovery–nothing in between. For example, an alcoholic sober for 14 months had cravings and thoughts about drinking. He told himself he was not motivated to recover, instead of simply accepting the truth that struggle and conflicts are common in recovery. He had to learn that even highly motivated people can experience changes in motivation, and that harsh self-judgments are unwarranted.

Making things worse than they really are, or 'awfulizing' is exaggerating problems and turning minor difficulties into major problems. For example, a cocaine addict who stayed clean from all drugs for nine months "smoked a joint." Although she did not use again after this brief episode, she thought her recovery program had failed.

Over-generalizing is assuming that if something is true in one instance, it applies to any similar situation. For example, a heroin addict sober for seven months "set herself up" by seeking out a male friend with whom she previously shot dope. She used dope only once, but initially viewed this as a sign of "total failure," and began to think she couldn't recover. A depressed man became terribly angry when he noticed bird dung on the windshield of his car, he told himself, just my luck, birds are always crapping on my car.

Selective abstraction is focusing only on errors, weaknesses, mistakes or failures and ignoring accomplishments or successes. The previous example also illustrates this concept. The addicted woman assumed that since she "gave in" one time and shot dope she could not recover. She had a hard time understanding that her seven months of clean time was evidence of success.

Catastrophizing or magnification exaggerates the meaning or importance of an event, expecting the worst outcome. For example, an alcoholic went on a three-day binge following one year of sobriety. He told himself "I got drunk, I threw away my recovery." He expected his family and AA friends to sharply criticize him and was surprised when they were understanding and encouraged him to get back on the sober track.

Jumping to conclusions is reaching an end judgment without knowing all the facts. For example, a cocaine addicted alcoholic with a history of several relapses re-entered treatment following a fairly long relapse period. She thought, "I relapsed many times before, I'm hopeless and can't be helped. I don't know if I'm capable of recovering." Just because it happened before doesn't mean it will happen again. Although the clinician and client should always take the history of relapses seriously, they should be careful in assuming the person will relapse again. We have seen many individuals with a history of multiple relapse regain and maintain their sobriety. Or, a depressed client may think, "I'll never get better," which is not necessarily true.

Emotional responses involve assuming negative thoughts or feelings reflect the way things really are. For example, if an alcoholic feels frustrated with his recovery and thinks he is not doing things right, it doesn't mean that he is "incompetent." Thoughts such as, "I feel guilty, I must be a rotten person" or, "I feel hopeless, I must really be hopeless" can be challenged.

Should statements create rules that affect thoughts, feelings or behaviors. For example, a drug addict tells himself he "should" always like NA meetings, "should" always "want" to stay clean, or "shouldn't" get upset with his family. Such statements can lead the person to judging himself harshly during those times that he cannot comply with his "should" rule. Or, a person who loses weight only to gain some of it back can judge herself negatively because she "should have known better" and stayed on her weight loss program.

Labeling and mislabeling is creating a negative self-image from mistakes or errors. A "failure" experience leads to the conclusion that the person is a "failure." For example, an alcoholic relapsed after a long period of recovery and told himself he was a "failure" rather than simply admitting that a mistake was made. The danger with this type of cognitive error is that the person may tell himself there is no use trying to get back on the sober track even after a substantial period of recovery. For example: Instead of saying "I made a mistake," the client thinks "I am a loser."

Personalization or self-reference is believing one is the center of attention, and if a lapse or relapse occurs, one will be "blamed" for what happened.

Absolute willpower breakdown means assuming that once willpower has failed, loss of control is inevitable. Although some addicted people lose total control over substance intake any time they use, many do not lose total control until the relapse progresses for a long time.

Body over mind means believing that once alcohol or drugs are in the body, physiology takes over and makes the person powerless to control substance use. Again, while some people will lose control after they use, whether for physiological and psychological reasons, others will not lose control at first. The client must know that while he cannot *consistently* control substance use, if he lapses, he should be careful not to talk himself into continued use.

Consequences of Using Substances

This is an adaptation of Marlatt's "Decision Matrix" in which the client who is thinking about using considers the possible consequences. The aim is to encourage rational decisions by helping the client clarify all the possible effects of substance use before an actual decision is made. Since some clients develop "positive outcome expectancies" regarding substance use, this may help them clearly see the total picture, including possible adverse affects. For example, a client who is thinking of how good it feels to get high on cocaine may see that a return to use will cause a loved one considerable distress. This, in turn, may serve as a motivator to stay sober. While some clients impulsively use substances, many do not and first struggle with the question "should I or should I not use?"

This exercise gives the client permission to talk about both perceptions of "positive effects" of substance use and negative ones. What often emerges from these discussions is the client's ambivalence and internal struggles over substance use.

Control-O-Log

The *control-o-log* is similar to the *drunk-(drug-)-o-logs* often expressed by alcoholics and drug addicted clients, except the focus is on positive coping mechanisms as opposed to substance use. This technique helps the client focus on when and how he successfully coped with a desire to use substances, or a high-risk situation. It identifies the coping mechanisms used to sustain recovery. The purpose is to help the client increase personal control over substance use decisions and to help him draw upon past successful experiences.

This technique is especially suited for group dialogues. A client presents an issue or situation involving a struggle with the desire to use. You can ask the group, "have any of you experienced a similar situation where you've been able to resist using alcohol or drugs?" The group not only provides support, but also gives practical ideas on how others have coped with a difficult situation.

Daily Relapse Prevention Inventory

The daily inventory is used in mutual support programs and aids many people's recovery. One approach involves answering these questions at the end of the day.

- Were there any clues (warning signs) present today suggesting that I am moving away from recovery and building up to substance use?
- Did I experience any "high-risk" situations today that could trigger a relapse if not managed?
- How satisfied am I with my recovery today? Is there anything I need to change now?

If the client responds positively to question 1 or 2, she can devise a plan to follow to reduce the chances of relapse. If the client is not satisfied with recovery, she can determine why and identify what she needs to change at this time.

DECISION MATRIX

The person writes about a specific behavior change in terms of different decisions that can be made. This can relate to alcohol or drug use, any other addictive behavior, changing a health care habit (e.g., following a diet or engaging in regular exercise), any interpersonal behavior (e.g., ending a relationships or addressing a specific conflict or problem with another person) or goal (e.g., get a new job, go back to school, get training, save money). The person writes down different options related to the behavior change such as:

- Short-term advantages or pros of making this change.
- Short-term disadvantages or cons of making this change.
- Long-term advantages or pros of making this change.
- Long-term disadvantages or cons of making this change.

MEDITATION

Meditation refers to a range of practices aimed at clearing the mind, promoting relaxation or calmness, building energy, developing positive emotions such as compassion, love, or forgiveness or reducing negative emotions such as anger, anxiety or depression. Many forms of meditation are available including, but not limited to Transcendental Meditation, Zen, Buddhist, Christian, Jewish, Taoist meditation, Hinduism and others. Each form is based on a particular set of beliefs and practices. Some require the person to remain still while others may involve praying, walking or listening to music. A person can attend a class on how to meditate or teach oneself.

Meditation can help reduce stress, calm or slow a person down, and improve overall physical, mental or spiritual health. Some forms such as "Loving-Kindness Meditation" help the person increase compassion towards oneself and other people (Note: see the Greater Good Science Center website for more information on meditation and mindfulness).

MINDFULNESS

Mindfulness refers to consciously focusing on the present moment in time so that a person is aware of internal thoughts, feelings, physical sensations in the body and the surrounding environment. This involves the ability to accept thoughts and feelings, including negative ones, without judgment. Mindfulness strategies and clinical programs teaching mindfulness skills are used for substance use disorders and many psychiatric disorders. Mindfulness has also been used for expectant parents, students in schools, and inmates in prisons, all of which experienced positive outcomes. Many studies show that practicing mindfulness can result in physical, psychological and social benefits such as:.

- Improvement in the immune system to fight off disease.
- Improved ability to cope with stress.
- An increase in positive and decrease in negative emotions.

- An improved ability to focus on tasks at hand.
- Improvement in symptoms of psychiatric disorders.
- Greater satisfaction in relationships.
- Improved habits that lead to weight loss.

Mood Thermometer

This involves tracking a mood or emotional state (anxiety, depression, mania) on a daily basis to rate its severity. This can also be adapted to any emotion (anger, boredom, loneliness) including positive emotions such as gratitude.

The mood or emotion is rated on a scale of 1–10 with 1 representing a very low level of the mood or emotion, 5 representing a moderate level, and 10 representing a very high level. Tracking moods or emotions over time can show patterns as well as improvements or setbacks. The client should agree on an acceptable baseline (e.g., "as long as my depression or mania are lower than a 4, I feel stable." If my depression or mania reach 5 or above, I need to take action or get help from my therapist or doctor, or peers in recovery").

Monitoring Persistent Symptoms of Psychiatric Illness

Developed by Dr. Robert Liberman, this monitoring process is similar to using a daily mood thermometer in that chronic or persistent psychiatric symptoms are identified and rated on a daily basis. These can include mood symptoms, psychotic symptoms (delusions or hallucinations), or cognitive symptoms (thoughts of wanting to hurt self or others, or negative, depressed thinking). The idea is to catch symptoms early when they begin to worsen and take action before a full blown episode of illness reoccurs.

The client can list and rate daily each persistent symptom of illness that is of concern. A cut-off point is decided so that the person knows to reach out and ask for help and support from others if symptom severity reaches a certain level (this usually means having a plan to intervene when mild symptoms become moderate or severe). For example, Brian said, "when my voices begin to feel like they are torturing me (which he rated as 7 or higher on a scale of 10), I know I'm getting sicker and need to talk with my therapist or doctor right away."

Relapse Autobiography

Many clinicians use autobiographies to get the client to reflect on the history and context of her substance use, and the effects. The relapse autobiography is a similar tool except that it focuses on the relapse experience(s) of the client.

In her own words, the client writes a detailed relapse history. This autobiography should contain information about: what substances were used, for how long, with whom, when, why they were used, and in what context. It should also include the period preceding the actual relapse to help the client determine what relapse warning signs occurred before the actual relapse. This time frame may vary among clients, but attention should be paid to changes in thinking, attitudes, emotions or behaviors preceding the relapse. Often, a client is less defensive when privately reflecting on a relapse experience in a writing exercise as opposed to in a group.

The relapse autobiography should portray the client's reaction to the relapse, including feelings and thoughts about herself as a recovering person. It should also touch on the effects of the relapse, both on the client and her family or significant others. Last, it should describe what happened following the initial period of substance use, that is, how she acted following the lapse. This task is easy to adapt for those who have difficulty expressing themselves in writing. For example you can ask the client to tape record her relapse autobiography.

Learning from Mistakes: Relapse Debriefing

Debriefing is similar to the process used in the *Relapse Autobiography* in that the client explores the details of lapses or relapses. Marlatt uses this process to deal with "serious temptation situations" in addition to actual slips. The clinician can explore the details surrounding the high-risk situation, alternative coping responses, and the client's reactions–affective, cognitive, and behavioral. Such an intervention provides an opportunity for the client to learn from past mistakes.

I (DD) find it helpful to help the client deal with the guilt and shame felt after a relapse. Some clients avoid discussing a relapse. One practical way to counteract this is to build into the therapeutic contract the expectation that all close calls, lapses and relapses must be reported and discussed. With few exceptions, my experience has been that if relapse is openly examined at the onset of treatment, and made part of the therapeutic contract, most clients will report lapses and relapses. In group therapy and multiple family sessions, such deliberations provide a valuable source of learning for all participants.

Relapse Fantasy

This technique involves exploring the client's dreams involving substance use, or asking the client to "imagine what it would take for you to return to alcohol or drug use." Such exploration helps the clinician assess the client's potential "high-risk" situations, how she perceives the possibility of relapse, and how she would think, feel or behave in a relapse situation. This information can then be used to help the client develop positive coping skills.

Relapse Prevention Workbook for Substance Use Disorders (RPW)

The RPW was developed by the author (DD) from an extensive review of the research, clinical and self-help literature on relapse and talks with hundreds of relapsed clients and professionals. The RPW is an educational aid for clients in treatment. It provides information on several relapse prevention and management topics and engages the reader in reading and writing tasks to relate the material in a personal way. The workbook can be used with clients in recovery for the first time as well as with those who have relapsed. It operationalizes many of the concepts from Marlatt's model of RP. The RPW is available in Spanish. A version for adolescents is also available. Following is a summary of the topics reviewed in this workbook.

Understanding the relapse process is an introduction to relapse as a process, and common clues or warning signs that may suggest the relapse process is in motion. This section also gives a case example, and asks clients who have relapsed to learn from their past experience by answering several questions.

Identifying "high-risk" factors introduces the person to the idea of anticipating "high-risk" situations that could trigger a relapse. An inventory of 66 items, based on an adaptation and expansion of Marlatt's categories of high-risk categories, is reviewed by the client. The high-risk categories include: 1) negative feelings, attitudes or thoughts; 2) social pressures to use alcohol or drugs; 3) sobriety plan or treatment related problems: 4) problems in relationships with other people; 5) urges, cravings, or testing my control; and 6) other high-risk situations.

Strategies for handling high-risk factors has the client prioritize high-risk factors and develop coping plans based on them. This section provides two case examples that illustrate coping strategies for high-risk situations.

Handling cravings for alcohol or other drugs helps the client identify signs and causes of cravings, and reviews practical coping strategies.

Handling social pressures to use substances prepares the client for direct and indirect social pressures faced during recovery.

Anger management in sobriety helps the client understand the connection between anger problems and a possible relapse. Anger is viewed as a problem from "within." The section provides a five-step problem solving process to help the client recognize and handle angry feelings.

Use of leisure time in sobriety helps the client begin to look at how to manage boredom and maintain active involvement in leisure pursuits that do not evolve around alcohol or drugs, or people who get high.

What to do if a lapse or relapse occurs focuses on plans to stop a lapse or relapse should one occur. Clients need concrete and easy-to-use strategies to take action should they use substances, regardless of how long the episode of use lasts.

Building a long-term sobriety plan focuses on mapping out a long-term recovery program to continue to change and reduce relapse risk. Recovery is not an easy or quick process for anyone, so accepting the need for long-term involvement helps reduce relapse risk if the client follows through with the plan.

Emergency sobriety card focuses on the importance of having specific people and organizations to call upon for help and support during difficult periods.

Lifestyle balancing and sobriety helps clients begin to examine the need to make global changes in lifestyle. An outcome of good recovery is improvement in the quality of life. Being more balanced can contribute to this quality.

A *daily relapse prevention inventory* asks the client to monitor relapse warning signs or high risk factors on a daily basis. This helps him remain vigilant about relapse warning signs and high-risk factors.

RELAPSE PREVENTION WORKBOOK FOR PSYCHIATRIC DISORDERS

This workbook helps the client understand relapse in psychiatric illness, and reviews 10 recovery strategies to facilitate recovery and reduce relapse risk. It includes additional sections on:

Causes of relapse, which reviews factors contributing to relapse—treatment-related, lifestyle, relationship, other factors.

Effects of relapse, which can relate to any area of health or functioning.

Red flags or warning signs of relapse, which reviews changes that may precede relapse of any psychiatric disorder—changes in thinking or thought processes, moods, health habits or daily routines, compliance with treatment, or behaviors.

Managing relapse warning signs, which includes identifying signs, developing an action plan to manage these, discussing the plan with others, and having an emergency plan should a relapse or recurrence happen.

Relapse and your family, which focuses on helping families or concerned others understand relapse and how they can help their loved one as well as cope with their reactions to a loved one's psychiatric illness or relapse.

OTHER READINGS (BIBLIOTHERAPY)

There is a large self-management recovery literature on all types of psychiatric disorders and related problems to help clients learn strategies to manage their disorders and improve the quality of their lives. Most include sections on relapse prevention since relapse and recurrence are common with psychiatric illness.

Readings increase a client's knowledge of recovery and RP and stimulate interest in using this information in recovery. *Bibliotherapy,* as this technique is called, has been used for years in treatment. Topics that are potentially threatening or difficult for some clients to talk about can often be presented in non-threatening ways through reading. Each clinician should develop a list of suggested readings relevant to various types of SUDs and co-occurring psychiatric disorders (readings from mutual support programs as well as those from professionals or others in recovery who share their knowledge or experiences).

ROLE PLAYS (BEHAVIORAL REHEARSALS)

Many of the issues that impact on relapse can be adapted to role plays to help clients increase their awareness of these issues and learn coping strategies. Virtually any problem that involves other people can be practiced in role-plays—refusing a request, making a request, dealing with anger, conflict or disputes in relationships, reaching out for help and support, sharing positive emotions, and others.

The clinician first discusses the problematic situation, or the one the client wants to change to get as much information as possible. The client then practices new responses in a role-play. The clinician can play the role of the "other" person, or the role of the client to "model" responses that seem too difficult for the client to produce. For example, a client may not be used to rationally or calmly expressing a feeling such as anger or disappointment to a family member or loved one. If so, it may be advisable to first see the clinician "role play" this situation.

Interpersonal role-plays are effective in groups as more clients can get involved in the role-play, supporting the person who is practicing new coping behaviors. Other clients, for example, are often more realistic than the clinician when enacting situations in which substances are offered to the client. Group role-plays provide other members situations with which to identify. Often, these role-plays lead to productive therapeutic discussions and rehearsal of positive coping strategies.

There are many variations of role-plays that the clinician can use. Some of these include:

Use another group member to verbally serve as the client's "alter ego" in the role-play. The clinician first gets the client's permission to do this. The person functioning as the alter ego speaks out loud during the role-play, saying what he thinks the client would like to say but is unable to. For example, in an actual role-play situation, a cocaine addict may be offered drugs by a friend. While he may say something such as "no thanks, I'm staying clean," he may be thinking, "I really want to get high. I really crave the drug." The alter ego expresses these inner thoughts or feelings, thus allowing conflicts to surface and be discussed. This process also helps the client understand the role of ambivalence in recovery, when mixed feelings surface.

Use another group member to serve as the role-playing client's "alter ego" by recording thoughts and feelings. This is similar to the method above except that the alter ego writes down thoughts and feelings, which are discussed after the role play ends.

Use dyads or triads to role-play problems identified by one or more clients. This makes all group members active participants in the role-play, and is less threatening than when done in front of large groups.

Role-plays usually work best when the clients choose the situations to practice. However, the clinician can have available several common scenarios–expressing anger, refusing substance use offers, asking for help or support when depressed, dealing with a relationship problem– which many clients identify with.

Another effective technique in role-plays with groups is to ask those not directly participating in the role-play to imagine that they are in the actual situation being enacted by other members. They are told to pay close attention to their thoughts and feelings, and to think about how they would handle the situation being role played.

At the end of role-plays I have found it useful to give the client a chance to talk about what the experience was like. What did he think? How did he feel? How effective did he think his responses were? What did he dislike about his responses? What did he like? The other members of the audience can also respond with feedback. This often provides an excellent opportunity for the group to mutually explore issues and problems that are commonly faced in recovery.

If there is sufficient time, and the situation permits, videotaping role-plays can be an effective tool for helping clients learn about themselves. They can dissect role-plays to learn what works best.

THE ROAD TO RELAPSE

This is a powerful way to illustrate the process of moving from recovery towards a relapse. While this exercise can be conducted in an individual session, I (dcd) developed it primarily for use in a group so that clients could learn from each others' experiences. The group leader asks the group who has relapsed following a period of sobriety in order to identify a specific person to illustrate the relapse process. It is best to use a client who was "in recovery" (i.e., had accepted the SUD, accepted the need to change, and worked a program of recovery) prior to the relapse as opposed to someone who was abstinent for just a few weeks or months, primarily for external reasons. The leader asks for a specific volunteer, which preferably should be a client with an extended period of recovery prior to the relapse (reality sometimes dictates that the volunteer may have had less than a year in recovery before relapses, but many times there will be clients with one or more years of sobriety who relapsed).

The group leader tells this client to recreate the relapse by remembering as much as possible about warning signs that preceded this relapse. The experience is recreated by having this client physically walk down an imaginary road from recovery towards relapse. Have the client imagine that this road has a fork in it, which has two paths—the lower path leads to substance use lapse and possible relapse; the upper road leads back to recovery. The client is then instructed to take one step down the road to relapse and state out loud a specific warning sign.

It is best to instruct the client ahead of time to use examples of both obvious warning signs (e.g., "I cut down or stopped AA meetings; I skipped group counseling sessions, then never returned") and those idiosyncratic to her relapse (e.g., "I became interested in a man who was still getting high; I started to become dishonest in my daily life"). Have the client take 4–6 steps, stopping after each one to state out loud the warning sign.

Then, ask the client to stand at the fork in the road, which represents the point in time a decision was made to use alcohol or drugs. Have the client discuss out loud what she was thinking and feeling prior to going down the bottom path in the road to a lapse or relapse. Ask the client to talk about what she used, when and where, how she feels, and what she thinks about the experience in retrospect. It isn't unusual for the initial description of substance use to be presented in a positive way ("it felt good to drink or catch a buzz, what a relief it was to smoke pot"). This is usually followed by a description of the negative consequences of the lapse or relapse ("I realized that I was messing up again, this will lead me to big trouble, I'll disappoint or hurt my children").

Once this process is finished, ask this client to discuss her reactions to this exercise and what she learned about the relapse process and what she could do in the future to manage warning signs without going down the path to lapse or relapse. Then, ask the other group members to share what they observed and what they learned. Ask them what they could do in a similar situation in the future. Focus both on early warning signs and being at the fork in the road, stressing that the earlier clients catch their warning signs, the greater the likelihood of a positive response. Often, clients who watch a peer conduct a walk down the road to relapse will relate to the experience of moving from recovery to relapse.

After the group has discussed this experience, have the same client repeat this exercise as closely as possible to the way it unfolded the first time. This time, have a support person (another client) walk next to her as she travels the road from recovery to relapse. Instruct this "helper" to make a supportive statement each time the client states out a loud a specific warning sign. For example, if the client says "I'm tired of going to AA meetings" as a warning sign, the helper might say "talk to an AA friend about what you think is going on to cause you to be tired of AA." Or, if the client says "I started thinking privately about how to get some cocaine," the helper might say "don't keep secrets; share your struggles with a sponsor, counselor or friend." The client is not to respond to the helper's comment but only listen to them.

Once the client and helper walk to the fork in the road, and the client shares the relapse experience, ask her if it felt different to have a support person with her during this trip down the road to relapse. Then, talk with the group about the difference between "going down the road to relapse alone" or "using support" from another person. You can then ask the group members, "What is the first word in Step 1 in the 12-Step program?" This often leads to an exploration of recovery as a "we" vs. an "I" process. Clients have choices—they can struggle alone or reach out for help and support from others. Although there are no guarantees, those who reach out for help and support do better than those who keep their struggles privately.

Sobriety Journal

The *Sobriety Journal* can help clients regularly monitor and review their recovery and progress, and write their thoughts, feelings and behaviors in a journal. Although a specific *Sobriety Journal* exists with a specific format, the clinician can also use a generic journal that is broad in focus. A client can record anything related to his recovery. However, the clinician can ask the client to record recovery issues, problems, or concerns such as temptations to use substances, cravings, or feelings about socializing with others who are using substances.

The journal provides a means for the client to ventilate feelings and reflect on experiences and reactions in recovery, particularly positive or successful ones. The client is instructed to make sure that successful experiences are recorded. These positive coping mechanisms are identified and built upon. The *Sobriety Journal* may help the client keep recovery in perspective, especially when recovery is perceived as going too slowly or if the client feels that few positive gains have been made.

I usually ask clients to regularly share with me whatever part of their journal they wish so that we can discuss their experiences. I give them the freedom to not share any parts of the journal, which they prefer to keep private. However, seldom has a client not wanted to share the journal.

An electronic journal has many features to stimulate the client and aid work in recovery. Following is an outline of this unique tool for individuals in various stages of recovery.

Write about your SUD and recovery. Write about your history of a SUD, treatment and recovery, or any other aspect of your life. Write as much as you want, as often as you want. You can organize your writing into categories such as family, emotions, relationships, spirituality, leisure interests, etc.

Regularly review your progress. Reflecting upon progress has always been encouraged by AA or NA through the use of a "daily inventory." You can review your recovery as often as you wish. In the early phases of recovery, more frequent reviews are recommended.

Reflect on your recovery and strategies to prevent relapse. Thinking about your recovery and actions to take to manage the challenges of recovery will reduce your relapse risk.

Daily tips. These provide food for thought for your recovery.

Quotes. These come from recovery writings (e.g., "Big Book" of AA or "Basic Text" of NA), professionals in the field of addiction, and well known individuals (writers, politicians, philosophers).

Daily Pulse. This allows you to track cravings, moods and many other aspects of your life and recovery. You can rate each item and write narrative comments as well.

Timeline. This can help you review your history of a SUD and recovery.

URGE OR CRAVING SURFING

This was developed by Dr. Alan Marlatt to help clients with any type of addiction "ride out" an urge (craving or desire) to use alcohol, tobacco or other drugs, or urge to engage in the addictive behavior the person is trying to change (gambling, sex, eating). The client is instructed to imagine that he is riding a wave, which represents the urge or craving experienced. By sticking with it and riding it out, the wave (urge) will eventually break (go away). This way, urges are managed one at a time. The client learns that urges do not persist and end. Each time the impulse to give in to an urge is resisted, the client will feel more confident about coping with the next urge.

This strategy can be adapted to other behaviors such as the desire to hurt oneself (cut or burn), a desire to take an addictive drug to quell anxiety, or the desire to let loose verbally with angry feelings and express things to others that can cause damage in the relationship. By riding out the desire to act in a way that can be harmful to self or others, the client's coping skills are strengthened.

Any of the aforementioned counseling aids or tools can help the counselor in conducting RP groups. Some of these can be given as homework assignments between sessions. Others can be used in a group session. These aids can be incorporated in treatment or recovery groups in all types of settings.

Clients respond favorably to "experiential" strategies as it enables them to learn more about their internal processes (i.e., what they think and how they feel). This also keeps and/or stimulates their interest in RP topics reviewed in groups, especially in programs in which clients are exposed to a large number of group sessions per week.

CHAPTER 5

RP Groups for Substance Use and Other Addictive Behaviors

CREATING RELAPSE PREVENTION GROUPS

Group treatments are used throughout the continuum of care in inpatient, residential and ambulatory treatment programs. Groups help clients acquire information, increase self-awareness, gain support from peers, and learn coping skills to manage the challenges of recovery and reduce relapse risk. RP groups can be integrated into existing services or programs. Many structured residential or ambulatory programs incorporate a "relapse track" in which RP issues are covered.

You can provide a "stand-alone" RP group as part of a residential or ambulatory (outpatient) treatment program. A RP group can focus on topics relevant to recovery or relapse. Other groups, such as therapy, process or problem solving groups, can focus on relapse issues as clients present their experiences with the relapse process during treatment.

For ambulatory programs that provide one group per week, a group session can be divided in two segments. One segment covers the RP topic. The other segment allows for an open discussion of the problems or concerns that clients currently face that affect their recovery or relapse potential.

GROUP INTERVENTIONS

Group leaders can use a variety of interventions in conducting RP group sessions. These include:

- Providing educational information (about SUDs, treatment, recovery and relapse).
- Facilitating group discussion and interaction among clients.
- Helping members relate to the RP concepts discussed in a personal way.
- Monitoring "close calls," strong urges or cravings, and lapse or relapse experiences.
- Validating issues or struggles contributing to lapse or relapse presented by group members.
- Emphasizing positive coping strategies used by members to aid recovery and prevent relapse, or intervene early in the process.
- Encouraging continuing participation in treatment, and attendance at mutual support programs such as AA, NA, other 12-Step or other non 12-step programs.

- Having members to talk directly to each other when sharing their opinions, discussing experiences or providing feedback related to topics of RP groups or problems discussed within the group.

- Asking group members to identify and practice new coping skills or RP skills (e.g., catching early signs of relapse, managing emotions, refusing substance offers, reaching out for help, etc.). Skills can be practiced within the group or outside the group.

GROUP FORMAT FOR OUTPATIENT SETTINGS

The following format is adapted from one of our large scale studies as well as our partial hospital and intensive outpatient programs. Changes can be made to this format based on the clinical characteristics of your clients (e.g., if your population is a Criminal Justice one, an item about adherence to their plan to meet with the probation or parole agent could be included; or, they could relate the topic of the session to behaviors that led to getting in trouble with the law).

Welcoming clients: The group leader welcomes members to the RP group session, states the topic and goals or objectives of the session. Any pertinent announcements are made to members.

Member introductions and check-in: Members state their name, drug and alcohol problem, date of last use, any strong cravings or "close calls" since the previous group meeting, any lapse or relapse to use, and meeting attendance since last session. Many programs have a chart on the wall listing these "check-in" items to help group members stay focused during this process. Other check-in items can be added based on type of group and time of sessions. The check in should take 10–20 minutes so that the majority of the session is spent on the topic of the session.

Substance use lapse or relapse: If a group member has used since the last session the group will briefly process the event and discuss a plan to reduce relapse risk. The goal of total abstinence is emphasized. The group leader has to resist the tendency to spend extensive time on members' relapses in structured recovery groups as this could easily consume most or all of the group time, which would lead to failure to cover the content of the RP group topic. However, group members' lapses or relapses can be used to illustrate points covered during the educational component of the session.

Handouts or assignments: Recovery and relapse prevention handouts from a workbook, journal or other source or behavioral assignments are briefly reviewed if assigned at the previous session. Since interactive recovery tasks take time, it is most efficient to assign these tasks prior to the RP group session so members can reflect upon the topic, and complete interactive tasks aimed at getting them to relate to the RP material. If members fail to complete an assignment this should be discussed in terms of the implications for recovery or relapse.

RP group topic introduction: The group leader introduces the RP topic and reviews the major points noted on the outline for the specific topic. Questions and interactive discussions are used throughout the session. Members are asked to share their reactions to the material presented. They are encouraged to discuss how the RP topic relates to their personal situations. Group members are encouraged to interact and offer feedback to one another when appropriate. Most of the session is spent on an interactive exploration of the material related to the group topic. This part of the group should last 45–60 minutes in 90 minute sessions. If groups are 60 minutes, this section should last 40–45 minutes. Make sure sufficient time is spent on "coping strategies" so that all or most of session is not spent only on the problems or struggles presented by clients relevant to the topic.

***Review of homework (optional)*:** In small groups (fewer than 10 members) members can briefly share answers to questions on the handouts provided if homework was assigned. This is optional as some groups can discuss the questions without using written handouts. The group leader has to control the flow so members are brief when they share their answers. Some members, for example, want to share extensive details, whether it is a personal craving, a relapse warning sign, or any issue related to recovery or relapse.

***Group ending*:** In the final 10–15 minutes of the group session, members state one thing they learned (information, idea, coping strategy) from the RP group and state their plans for recovery until the next session. Clients are encouraged to attend mutual support meetings, get and use a sponsor, get phone numbers from other AA/NA members, and actually call these members.

***RP assignment (optional)*:** Assignments related to the next session topic can be given to group members with a brief explanation as to what is required. These can be from a written guide (e.g., a workbook or recovery journal), a written handout (e.g., a sheet of paper with a few questions related to the next group session's topic) or a behavioral task (e.g., members are asked to talk to at least 1 or 2 other people in a mutual support program to find out how they managed substance cravings, resisted social pressures to use, or managed upsetting emotions that previously contributed to relapse).

***Serenity Prayer (optional)*:** The group joins hands and recites the Serenity Prayer aloud to end the session.

GROUP FORMAT FOR RESIDENTIAL OR INPATIENT SETTINGS

The group format depends on group size. Large groups conducted in rehab programs or hospitals in an auditorium or large room are more likely use a lecture format. However, even large groups can incorporate interactive tasks with clients such as brief interviews with a client related to the group topic, or sharing of experiences relevant to the group topic by someone with a sustained period of recovery. For example, a recovering person with several years of ongoing sobriety could be a guest in group and share their initial struggles with relapse warning signs or risk factors, then share what helped them deal with the issues in their ongoing recovery that led to preventing relapses.

Since some clients are in a supervised residential or inpatient environment, actual episodes of substance use are not likely (although they are possible) so focus can be more on what clients should learn about RP. They will have plenty of time to complete recovery assignments (reading, writing, behavioral) so these do not have to be completed during the RP group session. Group endings can focus mainly on sharing something they gained from the RP group sessions or one goal they will work on during the rest of the day or over the next few days.

ORIENTING CLIENTS TO RP GROUPS

Orienting clients to RP groups can help them prepare to get the most from the sessions. Orientation can include a review of any of the following in addition to questions or concerns of the client. The process can include the client signing an agreement to abide by the rules of the RP group.

- Purpose and goals of the RP Group.

- Types of RP group sessions and how these are conducted (structured RP topic, open- ended therapy or discussion group, etc.).

- Logistics of group (location and time), length of time or number of sessions the client will attend.

- How to get the most out of RP group sessions (e.g., come prepared with completed assignments or with problems to discuss, be honest during check-in periods, etc.).

- The importance of self-disclosure or talking about one's experiences, thoughts, feelings, behaviors and ideas relevant to RP topics, issues or problems discussed in group.

- Specific rules of the RP group such as coming on time, not leaving early, turning off cell phones during the session, not coming to group sessions under the influence of alcohol or other drugs, honestly reporting lapses or relapses and completing therapeutic assignments from journals, workbooks, readings, etc.

- Other issues (when a referral may be needed to a higher level of care based on poor compliance with treatment, lack of progress, a relapse etc.).

STRATEGIES FOR RP GROUP LEADERS IN COVERING GROUP CONTENT

Group leaders who use a broad repertoire of interventions can keep groups engaged, especially sessions that use a curriculum on a specific RP group topic. This may also help reduce burnout for clinicians who conduct multiple group sessions each week by enabling them to cover the material for clients in different ways.

These strategies include but are not limited to:

Brief lectures in which interactive discussions are initiated to get members to relate to the material presented. For example, when presenting information on "Relapse Warning Signs" elicit examples from group members on obvious and subtle warning signs preceding their past relapses. Get a variety of answers to show examples of signs.

Use of brief stories to illustrate points discussed during the session. These stories can focus on failure and success experiences. For example, if a group leader is discussing the importance of clients reaching out for help and support when experiencing strong cravings for drugs or alcohol, examples can be shared of a client who kept cravings to himself and eventually relapsed, and of a client who called an NA friend to talk about the strong craving and managed to stay sober as a result. *Guest speakers*. These may include professionals with different perspectives on relapse or recovery (e.g., a medical professional to discuss medication-assisted treatment for SUDs). Or, they can include others in recovery, especially treatment program graduates, who share their stories of recovery and relapse prevention strategies they used. When using others in recovery, make sure the person spends more time on the "story" of recovery and relapse prevention, and less time on the "story" *of substance use.* You can also have people share stories of inspiration or resilience. For example, I had a an elderly man share his experiences as a holocaust survivor with patients and clinical staff in several of our treatment programs. This led to many interesting suggestions relevant to dealing with problems and struggles in life.

Educational videos or audiotapes. These can be used to provide information, stimulate diaglogue or provide "role models" of others in recovery who share their stories of using positive coping strategies. Or, they can illustrate how others stopped a lapse or relapse. A brief video or audio material with interactive discussion is the most appropriate manner to use these to supplement other interventions. Group leaders should avoid using the majority of group time to show a video or play an audio. Most of the time in group should be spent discussing specific segments of these materials. For video or audiotapes longer than 15+ minutes, one strategy is to show or play a specific segment then follow this with participant comments before showing or playing another segment.

Use of written recovery handouts, workbooks or journals. Many programs use interactive materials to educate clients and engage them in relating written materials to their own situation. These provide information, raise self-awareness and help clients to learn coping strategies to manage problems and the challenges of recovery. It is best to have clients complete written handouts prior to the RP group session so the group time can be used to discuss what they learned from this written material and how they relate it to their recovery. Since group size varies, it is not necessary to ask every member to share answers to every question on a written assignment. The idea is to use the experience of group members to review specific materials assigned by having some members share their personal learning from completing a written assignment.

Use of recovery readings. Readings related to any topic covered in group sessions can be assigned or recommended between sessions or shared during a session, provided they are brief. Readings can come from many sources such as books, pamphlets, recovery guides, the internet or even novels. Readings may come from the "Big Book" of AA, the "Basic Text" of NA, other 12-Step related readings, or other readings on specific addictions (alcoholism, cocaine) or topics (anger, relapse, depression, cravings, family issues).

Role plays or behavioral rehearsals. Many interpersonal problems that contribute to relapse can be adapted for practice in role plays. These can relate directly to recovery such as refusing an offer for alcohol or drugs, asking for a sponsor or talking with a family member about one's SUDs and recovery. For example, a role play can be set up in which a friend offers alcohol (or drugs) to the person in recovery. The person being offered can be instructed to respond in any way that he wants. The person offering the substance can be instructed to exert strong pressure on this other person.

Role plays can also relate to other problems that impact on recovery such as addressing an interpersonal conflict, reaching out to a friend for support when feeling depressed, or learning to express anger in healthy ways that do not push others away or harm relationships.

Interpersonal role-plays enable group leaders to engage members not involved in the actual role play by asking them to imagine they are in the situation that is the focus of the role play. Group members can be asked to pay attention to what they think and feel, and how they might handle the situation illustrated in the role play. Often, these role-plays lead to productive therapeutic discussions and additional behavioral rehearsal of positive coping strategies relevant to the specific problem or issue that the role play focuses on.

Here are some variations of role plays that the group leader can use.

• *Use another group member to verbally serve as the client's "alter ego" in the role-play.* The clinician first gets the client's permission to do this. The person functioning as the alter ego speaks out loud during the role-play, saying what he thinks the client would like to say but is unable to. For example, in an actual role-play situation, a cocaine addict may be offered drugs by a friend. While he may say something such as, "no thanks, I'm staying clean," he may be thinking, "I really want to get high. I really crave the drug." The alter ego expresses these inner thoughts or feelings, thus allowing conflicts to surface, be discussed, and hopefully be resolved. This process also helps the client understand the role of ambivalence in recovery, when mixed feelings surface.

• *Use another group member to serve as the role playing client's "alter ego" by recording thoughts and feelings.* This is similar to the method above except that instead of the alter ego speaking out loud, thoughts or feelings are written down.

• *Use dyads or triads to role-play problems identified by one or more clients.* This makes all group members active participants in the role-play, and is less threatening than when done in front of large groups.

Role plays work best when the clients choose the situations to practice. However, the clinician can have available common relapse scenarios—expressing anger, refusing substance use offers–which clients identify with. Suggest these to the group if necessary.

At the end of role-plays ask the client to talk about what the experience was like. What did he think? How did he feel? How effective were his responses? What did he dislike about his responses? What did he like about his responses? The other members of the audience can also respond with feedback. This often provides an excellent opportunity for the group to mutually explore issues and problems that are commonly faced in recovery that are highlighted by the role play.

If there is sufficient time and the situation permits, videotaping role-plays can be effective for helping clients learn about themselves. They can dissect role-plays to learn what works best.

Monodramas. This refers to a technique in which a problem or issue is "externalized" and the thinking, emotions and behaviors of a client are explored. For example, when discussing craving to use alcohol or drugs, the group leader can ask for a client to volunteer to participate in an "empty chair" experience. The client is asked to "imagine your craving is sitting in this chair in front of you. Describe what it looks like, what it would say and how it would act. How would it make you feel? What would you say to it?"

A variation of this would be to ask the client to have a talk with the "substance craving sitting in the empty chair." The client can go back and forth between being the craving and being the client affected by it.

Creative media (arts, crafts, music). Many media can be adapted to express oneself related to the RP topics. Specific "themes" can be the focus of a session using creative media. For example, one of our creative and expressive arts therapists asks clients to create drawings or collages to illustrate their experience traveling down the "road to relapse."

Use of PowerPoint Slides. The use of slides can provide visual support for educational presentations on any topic conducted in a RP group session. This can take the focus off the group leader as members can shift from looking at the presenter to looking at the slides.

Slides can integrate information as well as visual materials that support the information provided. The possibilities for visuals on a PowerPoint slide are endless. Pictures of people, quotes related to the topic of the group, props (alcohol, drugs, places), cartoons, graphs and charts are just a few examples. This is especially helpful in large groups (e.g., in an auditorium or large meeting room where a lecture is provided to a large group of clients in a residential treatment program). However, slides can also be used in small groups (8–12 clients).

12 Structured RP Groups

In the sections that follow, we provide 12 RP group sessions that can be a "core" program or track within a residential or IOP program to address key issues of relapse and recovery. Each session can stand alone but, taken together, they provide a broad overview of important issues relevant to recovery and relapse. The *Relapse Prevention Workbook* can be used to supplement group sessions by having clients complete sections on the topic of the group sessions.

Most RP group topics can be conducted in multiple sessions to cover the material in greater detail if time permits. More group sessions on a specific topic also gives the leader time to have group members practice the skills being discussed. For example, for the topic "Establishing a Recovery Support System," additional sessions could be used to have members practice asking other for help and support with any type of problem or issue such as craving drugs, feeling depressed, wanting to act out on anger, etc.

Following is a brief review of these 12 group sessions.

The process and domains of recovery. This provides an overview of recovery and the areas clients should consider in developing their recovery plans as a way to reduce relapse risk.

Identifying and managing relapse warning signs. This helps members to understand relapse as a process, signs that precede relapse and focuses on the importance of taking action to manage warning signs.

Identifying and managing high-risk relapse factors. This covers the major categories of relapse risk factors and gets members to begin to identify their own, and begin to develop strategies to manage these.

Managing social pressures to use substances. Inability to refuse substance use offers is one of the highest relapse risk factors in recovery. This group helps prepare members to identify and manage the direct and indirect pressures they may face

Managing cravings to use substances. All RP models stress the importance of clients' learning to identify and manage substance cravings.

Managing anger. Inability to manage emotional states is the number one relapse factor (especially anger, anxiety, boredom, depression). Since anger is such a common problem among clients, this is addressed in a group session.

Managing boredom and using leisure time. This group helps members to understand ways to identify boredom and engage in substance-free activities.

Establishing a recovery support system. This session focuses on the need for a support system, and how to ask for help and support from people and organizations.

How mutual support programs help reduce relapse risk. These programs are the mainstay of long-term recovery for many addicted individuals. This session focuses on AA, NA, other 12-Step, and non 12-Step programs.

Managing setbacks. Since lapses and relapses occur, this group session helps members to understand the importance of preparing to intervene early should a lapse or relapse occur.

Building a long-term recovery plan. This promotes recovery as a long-term process and helps members to look at specific components of their plans. The importance of active participation in mutual support programs is emphasized.

Lifestyle balancing. This session helps members to review the major domains of life and to look at which ones are out of balance and could impact on relapse. Members then begin to plan ways to change one area out of balance.

THE PROCESS AND DOMAINS OF RECOVERY

Objectives

- Define recovery as a long-term process of "abstinence + change."
- Review the domains of recovery: physical, psychological, family, social and spiritual.
- Review internal and external aspects of change.
- Discuss how good recovery reduces relapse risk.

Discussion Points

Ask group members their view of the difference between "treatment" and "recovery."

Treatment involves: attending a program (e.g., detoxification, rehab or IOP), participating in counseling, taking medication for an SUDs, or a combination of these.

- It is provided by professionals and helps you get and stay sober and deal with problems caused or worsened by your SUDs.
- Treatment helps you understand and engage in recovery.
- Treatment helps you learn recovery skills to sustain your sobriety over time.
- Multiple episodes of treatment may be needed to help you sustain long-term recovery.

Recovery is a long-term process of *abstinence + change*. Ask group members what this means.

Ask members their view of the importance of abstinence from all substances.

- Discuss why abstinence from all substances (alcohol, street drugs and non-prescribed drugs) is recommended not just the "primary" drug of choice (if there is one).
- Any substance use can affect relapse to the primary drug of SUDs or lead to developing a SUD to another substance.

Ask group members to share their views of recovery as a *"long-term"* process.

- Treatment may be short-term (e.g., 5 days of detoxification, 21 days of residential rehab), but recovery continues to prevent relapse AND improve the quality of life.
- For SUDs, it is best to view recovery as occurring for years. Many engage in recovery programs such as AA, NA for their entire life.

Ask members to identify and discuss coping strategies to deal with periods of low motivation. You can also have members discuss barriers to "using" positive coping strategies.

- Reminding oneself of the negative effects of SUDs on self, family and others.
- Reviewing the benefits of sobriety, both short- and long-term.
- Repeating one's goals and how important sobriety is in reaching these goals.
- Accepting motivational struggles as normal and remaining patient.
- Admitting motivational struggles and sharing them with others who understand.
- Talking every day to AA, NA, CMA, CA friends or sponsor (or peers in other programs).
- Reading inspirational literature or recovery literature.
- Maintaining recovery disciplines even in the face of declining motivation.

Review the *physical domain of recovery*.

- Good nutrition.
- Regular exercise.
- Getting adequate sleep and relaxation.
- Taking care of medical problems (including pain), or dental problems.
- Learning to cope with cravings to drink alcohol or ingest drugs.
- Using medication-assisted treatment for SUDs to alcohol, nicotine or opioids.

Review the *psychological domain of recovery*.

- Accepting the SUDs and need for help and support from others.
- Learning to cope with problems and stresses without relying on substances.
- Changing distorted, negative or "stinking" thinking.
- Managing emotions without relying on substances.
- Getting help for psychological problems or psychiatric disorders.

Review the *family domain of recovery*.

- Reviewing the effects of SUDs on the family and individual members.
- Involving the family in treatment and recovery.
- Improving relationships with family members.
- Making amends when appropriate (with the input of a sponsor or therapist).

Review the *social domain of recovery*.

- Developing relationships with sober people.
- Learning to resist pressures from others to use substances.

- Developing healthy social and leisure interests to occupy time.
- Reaching out to others for help and support (peers in recovery, family, confidante).

Review the *spiritual domain of recovery.*
- Relying on a Higher Power for help and strength.
- Developing a sense of purpose and meaning in life.
- Taking other steps to improve one's faith or "inner life."
- Engaging in religious or faith based practices.
- Praying, meditating, reading spiritual literature.

Discuss how recovery is best viewed as a *"we" process* in which you use the support of others, especially sober individuals who are actively working a program of recovery.

Ask for examples of change that may occur in any of these domains of recovery.
- Internal change refers to changes within oneself (how you think or manage emotions).
- External change refers to changes in relationship and lifestyle.
- Positive changes lead to "good" recovery, which can reduce relapse risk.

MANAGING CRAVINGS TO USE SUBSTANCES

Objectives

- Define cues, triggers, or precipitants of cravings or urges to use alcohol or drugs.
- Identify external and internal precipitants of cravings.
- Review strategies to manage cravings to reduce relapse risk.

Discussion Points

Cravings, urges or desires to use substances are common during periods of recovery. *Overt* cravings are those that members can easily identify. *Covert* cravings are those that may show in others ways (irritability, low motivation, wanting to leave a program against professional advice).

A key component of RP is learning to manage these without using substances.

Ask group members to define and describe cravings for alcohol or drugs.

- How do cravings show in physical symptoms?
- How do cravings show in their thoughts?
- How do cravings show in their behaviors?

Ask group members to identify external factors that trigger their cravings and ask for specific examples for each category.

- *People:* people they used with, dealers, spouse or partner who uses or gets high.
- *Places:* parties, clubs, bars, any location associated with using substances.
- *Events:* family or work functions, concerts, events where substances are used.
- *Things or objects*: alcohol, drugs or things associated with drinking, using drugs or preparing drugs (papers, pipes, needles, any drug paraphernalia).

Ask group members to identify internal factors that trigger their cravings and ask for specific examples for each category.

- Thoughts: "I need a drink or drug; I'm dying to get high; I have to use to get through the day. I can't cope without something."
- Feelings: boredom, anxiety, loneliness, depression, anger.
- Physical pain or discomfort.

Discuss levels of intensity of cravings (from mild to severe). The level of craving will determine coping strategies to use.

Review how drugs "hijack" the reward system of the brain, which results in substances bringing more pleasure than food, sex, or other activities.

One result of this hijacking is the susceptibility to "cravings" when experiencing memories of substance use or exposed to external triggers.

This hijacking helps to partially explain the "compulsion" to use substances despite the damage they cause.

- Ask members to describe experiences with a compulsion to use alcohol or other drugs.
- Ask members to discuss at what level of intensity they believe it is difficult to manage their cravings to use substances and they are at risk for relapse.

Discuss the importance of using multiple strategies to manage cravings since one strategy may not work in every instance of a craving.

Review coping strategies to manage cravings by asking group members to share examples of times in which they successfully managed a craving such as:

- Recognize and label your craving for alcohol or drugs and accept these as normal.
- Keep a daily craving log in early recovery in order to remain vigilant and track your triggers and cravings and their intensity.
- Talk about your craving and thinking with a sponsor or confidante so you do not keep it a secret and let it overwhelm you.
- Go to a mutual support program meeting such as AA or NA (or non 12-Step program).
- Talk to others in recovery to find out what they do to manage their cravings.
- Talk yourself through the craving ("this will pass," "I can resist using," "I control my craving, it does not control me" or "one craving at a time").
- Remember how far you have come in your recovery and how good you will feel if you stick with it and don't give in to your craving for drugs or alcohol.
- Accept that your craving will pass in time and that most last just a few minutes.
- Redirect your activity to distract yourself temporarily from your craving.
- Write your thoughts about your craving and your related feelings in a journal.
- Get rid of booze, drugs, and drug paraphernalia (external triggers).
- Avoid high-risk people, places, events and things when having strong cravings.
- Pray or use your Higher Power and ask for help and strength.
- Read recovery literature to stay focused on your sobriety.

Ask group members to discuss why they sometimes have given in to cravings in the past and other times resisted them.

- What can they learn from these experiences?
- What determines "not giving in" or "giving in" to a craving?
- How do they feel when they "give in?"
- How do they feel when they "resist" their cravings?

Optional

Have group members shut their eyes and imagine their craving as some solid object. Then, ask them to imagine driving a truck or tank and crushing the craving. Discuss reactions to this exercise once it is finished and stress the importance of not letting their cravings (or SUDs) dictate their behaviors.

Have members share some of their responses to Section 5 "Managing Cravings for Substances" in the <u>Relapse Prevention Workbook</u>, pages 9–10. Remind them to use some of the craving management strategies listed on page 10.

Group Session

MANAGING ANGER

Objectives

- Define the three components of anger: feelings, thoughts and behaviors.
- Identify connections between anger and relapse.
- Review causes and effects of anger and the ways in which it is managed.
- Review strategies to manage or cope with anger from other people.

Discussion Points

Ask group members to define anger and discuss the degree to which it is a problem for them.

- Some will report chronic problems with anger and state they have a "short fuse."
- Others will state they have difficulty allowing themselves to feel angry or express it.

Ask members how mismanaged anger can impact on relapse or create other problems in their lives.

Relate their answers to anger having three components.

- Emotional (feelings like hurt, resentment).
- Cognitive (thoughts and beliefs).
- Behavioral (actions).

Discuss what group members learned from parents and others about anger and how to express it or deal with it in their relationships with others.

Review unhealthy and healthy ways of expressing anger:

- *Unhealthy*: acting out and hurting others physically or verbally; hurting oneself; being passive and letting anger build up; drinking or using drugs; and acting in passive-aggressive ways.
- *Healthy*: expressing it to others in a controlled manner when it is appropriate to do so; talking about feelings with a confidante; talking oneself out of being angry; engaging in activity that helps release or control anger; praying; or using anger as a motivator.

Ask group members to give examples of the effects of unhealthy anger management strategies on themselves and others.

- *On self*: using substances, becoming enraged, depressed, or out of control.
- *On others*: causing fear or worry, pushing others away, causing emotional damage in a relationship or causing it to end.

Discuss the connection between anger and methods of expression, and substance use.

- Anger can lead to substance use and be an excuse for relapse.
- Anger that controls a person can lead to acting out in ways that hurt others emotionally or physically.
- Anger that is not dealt with and suppressed can contribute to depression, self-harm, anxiety, low self-esteem, or internal turmoil.

Review strategies for managing anger and elicit examples from group members on both positive and negative ways they have dealt with their anger.

- *Verbal strategies*: talking about it directly with the person one is angry at; talking with a confidante to release feelings in a safe context; or getting support and another person's perspective.
- *Cognitive or self-talk strategies*: changing thoughts, internal dialogue or core beliefs; or, using the slogans of AA, NA or DRA (e.g., "this too shall pass").
- *Behavioral strategies*: going for a walk or exercising, redirecting one's activity, working around the house, praying or meditating, or going to an AA, NA, or DRA meeting to "drop off" anger.
- *Medications*: when anger is intense, persistent, and acted upon impulsively or aggressively, a mood stabilizer may be useful. An evaluation by a psychiatrist can determine if medications are needed for a psychiatric illness that contributes to these emotional problems.

Review a process to deal with angry feelings:

- Step 1: recognize anger in thoughts, feelings and behaviors.
- Step 2: examine causes of anger.
- Step 3: evaluate the effects of anger and coping strategies used.
- Step 4: identify coping strategies to manage anger in each situation.
- Step 5: rehearse or practice new coping strategies.
- Step 6: put these into action, evaluate their effects, and change as needed.

Optional

Create role plays in which a client has to deal with anger towards a stranger (e.g., a server in a restaurant who is rude), friend or family member (e.g., something they said or did to the client was hurtful and led to feelings of anger). Focus on using healthy verbal strategies to talk with another person about the situation contributing to the anger or the feeling itself (e.g., usually it is best to focus on the situation with people who are not intimate in the client's life).

Identify concerns of group members related to dealing with anger expressed by others.

Discuss strategies to cope with anger from other people.

Have members share some of their responses to Section 6 "Managing Anger" in the <u>Relapse Prevention Workbook</u>, pages 11–13. Remind them to use some of the anger management strategies listed on page 13.

Group Session

MANAGING BOREDOM AND USING LEISURE TIME

Objectives

- Identify ways that boredom affects recovery and can impact on relapse.
- Identify sources of boredom and "high-risk" times.
- Review the importance of structure and routine in daily life.
- Review strategies to manage boredom and engage in substance-free social activities.

Discussion Points

Ask group members to identify and discuss how boredom affects recovery from a substance use disorder. Problems associated with boredom include:

- Relapse to alcohol or drug use.
- Feeling depressed.
- Getting involved in activities that may temporarily reduce boredom but create other problems.
- Getting involved with people you used substances with in the past who may pose a threat to your recovery.
- Making major decisions that are not well thought out that or based on feeling bored (e.g., ending important relationships or quitting a job without having another job).

Discuss how group members feel about living without alcohol or drugs, or partying.

- They may miss the company of people they used or got high with.
- They may miss the action of bars or parties.
- They may feel nothing can replace the high feeling produced by alcohol or drug use.
- They may even feel "empty" at first, like life has little meaning or direction.

Identify and list leisure activities given up due to the substance use disorder.

- Why did they give up certain activities?
- Which of these do they miss the most?
- Which of these could be regained?

Identify drug-free or non-substance activities or situations that bring pleasure or enjoyment, or are fun. Discuss how or why these activities bring pleasure, enjoyment or meaning.

- Social
- Interpersonal

- Athletic
- Creative & Artistic
- Musical
- Spiritual
- Collecting
- Fixing or repairing things (cars, furniture).
- Other.

Identify and discuss the benefits of having structure in daily life.

- Reduces the chances of engaging in high risk situations causing relapse.
- Gives a sense of direction and purpose.
- Forces you to focus on goals and methods to achieve these goals.
- Necessitates accountability with your time.

Review practical coping strategies to reduce boredom.

- Recognize boredom, high-risk times for it and reasons for boredom.
- Regain "lost" activities that are not substance-related.
- Develop new leisure interests or hobbies.
- Learn to appreciate the simple pleasures in life.
- Build fun or pleasant activities into day-to-day life.
- Change thoughts and beliefs about boredom.
- Change thoughts and beliefs about involvement in drug-free activities.
- Evaluate relationship or job boredom before making major life changes.
- Deal with persistent feelings of boredom.
- Participate in recovery support groups or recovery clubs.

Discuss the issue of "emptiness" and "joylessness" associated with giving up substances, and how this contributes to both boredom and an inability to experience pleasure in normal activities.

Optional

Have group members complete a daily or weekly activities schedule to get them to practice building structure and activities into their daily lives.

Create role plays in which a client asks another person (family member or friend) to participate in a non-substance leisure activity. A variation of this is to have a client role play a situation in which he is invited to participate in a leisure activity that could threaten his sobriety (e.g., event where alcohol flows freely or others will be using drugs).

Have members share some of their responses to Section 7 "Managing Boredom and Using Leisure Time" in the <u>Relapse Prevention Workbook</u>, pages 14–15. Remind them to use some of the strategies to manage boredom listed on page 15.

MANAGING SOCIAL PRESSURES TO USE SUBSTANCE

Objectives

- Teach group members to anticipate direct and indirect social pressures to use substances.
- Identify the effects of social pressures on thoughts, feelings, and behaviors.
- Teach group members about "relapse set-ups" or how they put themselves in high risk social pressure situations either consciously or unconsciously.
- Review strategies to refuse social pressures to use alcohol or other drugs.

Discussion Points

Social pressure to use substances is one of the most common relapse risk factors with substance use disorders.

- Social pressure can be direct in which drugs or alcohol are offered to you.
- Social pressure can be indirect when others are using and you feel some pressure to use.
- However, it is not the social pressure itself, but your ability to manage it that determines if you will relapse and use alcohol or drugs.

Ask group members to provide examples of direct and indirect social pressures they have faced or expect to face in the future. These will fall in one of these categories:

- *People*: family members or friends who use; people with whom group members drank or got high, and drug dealers.
- *Places*: bars, parties or other places where substances were used.
- *Events or situations*: weddings, graduations, holiday celebrations, sporting events, concerts, or family events.

Set up role-plays where a member is offered alcohol or drugs by another person.

- Ask other group members observing the role-play to identify with the client being offered substances, and to pay attention to their thoughts and feelings.
- Have the group members being offered drugs or alcohol to respond based on how they feel at the moment.

After the role-play, process it with the group. Focus on the following:

- What do you feel when confronted by social pressures to use?
- What thoughts come into your mind when you are offered alcohol or drugs?
- How do social pressures impact on your motivation to stay sober?
- What can you do to refuse offers of substances?

Option: have group members pair up in dyads. Each offers the other alcohol or drugs. After this experience, discuss the same questions listed above.

Option: use a male-female in the role play and instruct the individual offering alcohol or drugs to add an offer of a "good time" or sex.

- A male client might feel more vulnerable to an offer by a female to get high because of the association between sex and getting high with a woman (or vice versa).
- A variation is to use male-male or female-female scenarios in order to address social pressures experienced by gay men and lesbian women.

Discuss what could happen if the group member gives in to social pressure.

- Could continue use and relapse.
- Could experience negative effects: medical, family, psychological, spiritual, legal, and financial.
- Could lose desire to get back on track.

After the group processes the role-play, review positive coping strategies:

- Avoidance of high-risk social pressure situations when appropriate.
- Verbal (ways to say no).
- Behavioral (ways to reduce or deal with unavoidable social pressures).
- Stress the importance of preparing by anticipating social pressures AND having coping strategies to use to manage these pressures.

Also, discuss the issue of "ambivalence" ((i.e., this role play often helps group members realize that part of them that still wants to get high and they "miss the action").

Ask group members why social support is so important during the holidays.

Discuss strategies to manage holidays such as:

- Spending them with supportive family and friends who do not threaten your sobriety.
- Remaining active in recovery program activities such as meetings or events.
- Participating in special events sponsored by mutual support programs like AA or NA.
- Being more vigilant about your sobriety and recovery.
- Planning ahead to feel prepared for holidays perceived as the most risky for group members.

Optional

Have members share some of their responses to Section 8 "Managing Social Pressures to Use Substances" in the <u>Relapse Prevention Workbook</u>, pages 16–17. Remind them to use some of the strategies to resist social pressures listed on page 17.

<u>Group Session</u>

ESTABLISHING A RECOVERY SUPPORT SYSTEM

Objectives

- Identify the benefits of having a recovery support system.
- Identify supportive people and organizations to include in a recovery support system.
- Identify reasons why it may be difficult to ask others for help or support.
- Identify ways to approach others and ask for help or support.

Discussion Points

Many mutual support programs exist to aid recovery and reduce relapse risk. All of these programs have "tools" to help the person recover.

Many people find the 12 Step fellowship of AA, NA, and CA helps their ongoing recovery.

- Meetings, sponsors, friendships with peers in recovery, the 12 Steps, slogans and recovery literature are all "tools" of 12-Step recovery that can help you stay sober and make positive changes over time.
- Others find non 12-Step programs helpful in their recovery (Women for Sobriety, SMART Recovery, Rational Recovery, etc).

In addition, other people and organizations can also provide you with help and support. These people do not have to be associated with a recovery program.

Then ask group members to give examples of people they might ask for help and support.

- Specific family members
- Specific friends
- A boss or coworker
- A neighbor
- A priest, minister or rabbi
- Other people?

Ask members of the group to give examples of organizations or groups that can play an important role in their efforts to stay sober and change their lifestyle.

- Church or synagogue
- Sports team
- Club that evolves a specific interest
- Volunteer organizations

Ask group members to give examples of how other people and organizations can play a role in their recovery.

- Other people can listen to their problems or concerns.
- Other people can be asked for specific help with a problem or situation.
- Other people can participate in mutually-satisfying activities or events that do not evolve around alcohol or drug use (e.g., share a hobby, go to a movie together, etc.).
- Organizations can give a sense of belonging.
- Organizations can offer opportunities for social interaction, a chance to develop new friendships or interests, or a chance to learn new skills.
- Church related organizations can provide an opportunity for spiritual growth.
- Other?

Ask group members to give examples of people they <u>should not ask for help</u> or support.

- Others who still get drunk or high and have no interest in supporting them in recovery.
- People who are angry at the recovering person and may still be holding a grudge.
- People who don't want the recovering person to succeed at getting or staying sober.
- Other?

Ask the group to give reasons why it is difficult to reach out and seek help or support from others.

- Fear of rejection.
- Feeling unworthy to be helped by others.
- Don't know how to be assertive and make requests to other people.
- Feeling shy and awkward.
- Embarrassed to have to ask another for something.
- Fear of sounding inadequate.
- Hard to trust others and open up.

Ask members to share ideas on how to "reach out" to others for help and support.

- Make a list of people that they trust and feel they can rely on.
- Choose one or two to start with in terms of asking for help or support.
- Talk with them about recovery and the need for their support.
- Communicate regularly, not just in time of trouble.
- Talk face-to-face, by phone, email or text messaging.

- Take a risk and open up to others.
- Also, show an interest in their lives.

Optional

Create role plays in which a member: a) asks for help and support from a friend, family member or confidante; or b) asks a member of AA or NA to be a sponsor.

- Then, discuss what the experience was like.
- What were the barriers to reaching out for help and support?
- Who are the people to reach out for to get help and support in recovery?
- What are ways to reach out (i.e., what can the members say?).

See Section 5 "Sober Friends and Social Support in Recovery" in the workbook Sober Relationships and Support Systems in Recovery, pages 11–12.

How Mutual Support Programs Aid Recovery and Reduce Relapse Risk

Objectives

- Provide an overview of the 12-Step and non-12-Step mutual support programs.
- Discuss experiences and beliefs about 12-Step programs
- Emphasize the importance of "we" in the "fellowship" of these programs.

Discussion Points

Ask members what types of mutual support programs they can use to aid recovery and reduce their risk of relapse.

- 12-Step programs (AA, NA).
- Mention that some areas have "specialty" mutual support programs for Native Americans, Christians, Gays and Lesbians, and other groups of people. These programs take into account some of the differences among people that can affect recovery.
- Other programs (Rational Recovery, SMART Recovery, Women for Sobriety).

Ask group members to share their experiences and beliefs about mutual support programs.

- What types of mutual support programs and meetings did they attend?
- What did they dislike about these programs?
- What did they like about these programs?
- What did they find helpful?
- Which of these programs can aid their long-term recovery?

Discuss how 12-Step programs are a major source of support in ongoing recovery from SUDs. These programs involve many components such as:

- Meetings (open, closed, leader, discussion)
- Sponsorship
- 12-Steps
- Recovery events
- Readings on SUDs and recovery such as "Big Book of AA" "Basic Text" of NA.
- Slogans such as "One day at a time," "This too will pass," or "Easy does it."
- Service

Get group members to discuss experiences and beliefs about 12-Step meetings.

- How often they attended or think they should attend.
- Types of meetings they liked the most (or least) and why.
- Why having a "home group" is important.
- Why regular meeting attendance is important.

Ask group members to discuss experiences and beliefs about sponsors.

- Why get a sponsor and how a sponsor can help.
- How to get a sponsor.
- Reservations about getting and trusting a sponsor.
- How to actively "use" a sponsor to mentor them in recovery.
- The difference between a sponsor and a therapist or counselor.

Get group members to discuss experiences and beliefs about the 12-Steps.

- Purpose of the 12-Steps.
- Focus on the "we" that is in all steps vs. the "I" to stress the "Fellowship."
- Which of the 12-Steps have members "worked" before and what was the outcome?
- Focus on the importance of "Step 1" during early recovery.

Ask members to share experiences attending events sponsored by the 12-Step Fellowship.

- Types of events attended (social, recovery oriented).
- What they gained from these events.
- How these events aided their recovery.
- How holiday related events can help them through difficult time periods.

Get group members to discuss experiences and beliefs about reading recovery literature.

- What have they read?
- How has recovery literature helped them?
- Mention the "Big Book of AA" and the "Basic Text of NA" for drug SUDs.
- State that there are many books, pamphlets and workbooks available related to the 12-Step program of recovery through AA, NA and other publishers.
- Inform group members where they can get 12-Step recovery literature.

Ask group members to discuss some of the "slogans" used in the 12-Step program.

- What are slogans and how can they help in daily recovery?

- Review a few of the common ones that help in early recovery.
- "Easy Does It; One Day at A Time; Let Go and Let God."
- "Think Through the Drink/Drug; This Too Shall Pass" and other slogans.

Get group members to discuss experiences and beliefs about "service."

- How do members "serve" each other?
- Service can be formal (chair meetings).
- Service can be informal (help set up and clean up after meetings).
- Service gets recovering person to focus on others rather than self.

Emphasize the "fellowship" is a "we" program and discuss what this means to group members to work "with" others in recovery rather than try to recover alone.

Optional

There are many excellent readings from AA, NA or other mutual support programs that can be used. Also, see the workbook "Using 12-Step Programs in Recovery", which provides an overview of SUDs, treatment, recovery and 12-Step programs (meetings, sponsorship, 12-steps, slogans, service, recovery resources).

IDENTIFYING AND MANAGING RELAPSE WARNING SIGNS

Objectives

- Teach group members that warning signs precede substance use relapse.
- Introduce the idea that relapse is a process as well as an event.
- Review *common warning signs* associated with relapse.
- Review *subtle warning signs* that may be unique to each individual.
- Identify strategies to manage relapse warning signs.
- For those who have had one or more episodes of relapse, teach them to use this as a *learning experience* to help their future recovery.

Discussion Points

Ask group members to define lapse or relapse as it relates to their substance use disorder. Give the following definitions:

- A lapse refers to the initial period of use and may or may not progress to a full-blown relapse.
- SUDs relapse refers to the process of returning to regular alcohol or drug use after a period of sobriety. A relapse can be brief or last very long.

Ask group members who have relapsed for examples of relapse warning signs from past experiences. Add additional examples as needed and state that warning signs will fall in the following categories:

- *Chang*es in thinking: "I don't need recovery, it's not worth the effort, I don't need medications anymore;" increase in severity of obsessions to drink or use drugs.
- Changes in mood: significant increase in anger, anxiety, boredom, or depression.
- Changes in health habits or daily routines: not taking care of personal hygiene or changes in daily habits or rituals.
- Changes in behavior: stopping or cutting down on treatment sessions, medications, or support group meetings without prior discussion with a professional or sponsor; reducing social interactions or activities; or reduced use of the "tools of recovery."

For relapse to substance use, emphasize it seldom "comes out of the blue."

- Discuss the context of relapses (who, where, when).
- Help group members see that it may be days or longer between an emergence of warning signs and substance use.

Emphasize the importance of catching relapse warning signs early.
- The earlier that group members intervene, the less likely that relapse will occur.
- Ignoring warning signs is not a good strategy as they must be dealt with.

Discuss the importance of not keeping warning signs a secret as things can build up and end in a relapse. Failure to identify or deal with relapse warning signs invites problems.

Discuss the difference between "common" and "individual or personal" warning signs. Elicit examples from each category.
- Common warning signs include cutting down or stopping mutual support meetings, counseling or medication-assisted treatment for SUDs.
- Individual or personal warning signs may include an increase in dishonestly, or depression during the holidays.

Ask group members to identify strategies to manage relapse warning signs. Their specific examples should fall in the following broad categories:
- *Cognitive*: changing thoughts and beliefs (e.g., challenging the thought "I can't have fun without alcohol or drugs" or "just because I didn't get the job I wanted doesn't mean I have to get depressed and give up").
- *Behavioral*: changing a behavior (e.g., resuming regular meeting attendance when one identifies cutting back as a warning sign; taking medications as prescribed after one identifies cutting down or stopping without first discussing this with a doctor or therapist).
- *Interpersonal*: seeking help and support from others in AA or NA (e.g., talking with others about ways to manage warning signs).

Use this information to emphasize the importance of *being aware of warning signs* and having a plan to manage them.

Discuss the importance of *seeking support from others* to manage warning signs (e.g., AA or NA friends and sponsors, counselor, friends, family, etc.).

Discuss the importance of *learning from past experiences* with lapse or relapse. If a group member has had multiple relapses following periods of recovery, the group leader can suggest that she review the most recent ones to see if there are any patterns to her behavior that indicate a relapse was likely to happen. Focus should also be on coming up with strategies to manage past warning signs that may occur in the future.

Optional

Have members share some of their responses to Section 2 "Understanding the Relapse Process in the Relapse Prevention Workbook, pages 2–4. Remind individuals with a history of multiple relapses to use this information to examine several relapses to help them determine if there is any pattern to their relapses.

IDENTIFYING AND MANAGING HIGH RISK FACTORS

Objectives

- Review factors that increase the risk of relapse to SUDs and label these as "high risk."
- Teach group members that relapse risk factors fall into different categories, but it is usually a combination of factors, rather than just one, that leads to relapse.
- Emphasize the importance of learning and using active coping skills to manage relapse risk factors.

Discussion Points

Relapse is common with substance use disorders.

- Relapse does not mean failure.
- It is common with chronic or recurrent disorders (medical, psychiatric or SUDs).

There are a number of external and internal factors that increase group members' vulnerability to relapse. These are referred to as "high-risk" factors.

Ask group members to identify high-risk relapse factors in relation to their SUDs

- These are situations in which they used alcohol or drugs in the past.
- These can occur regardless of how engaged you are in a recovery program.
- These are situations that increase their desire to use or lower their interest in recovery.

Review the major categories of causes of relapse, eliciting and giving some examples from each category:

- Negative emotional states (anger, anxiety, boredom, depression, etc).
- Social pressures to use alcohol or drugs.
- Strong urges, cravings or desires to use alcohol or drugs.
- Relationship conflicts (family, friends, others).
- Physical pain or discomfort.
- Positive emotional states.
- Lifestyle factors (health habits, structure, etc.).

Group members need more than awareness of their high-risk relapse factors. They also need to *actively use coping skills to* manage these factors effectively. Ask them why they think coping skills are necessary to reduce relapse risk?

The specific coping skills needed by group members will vary and depend on their relapse risk factors.

Stress the importance of having a plan to deal with potential high-risk factors. They are usually situations in which alcohol or drugs were used in the past. The idea is to:

- Identify (anticipate) high-risk factors.
- Examine the details of these high-risk factors.
- Develop strategies to manage relapse-risk factors.
- Implement coping strategies into daily recovery.
- Change strategies that do not work and try new ones.
- Learn from peers steps they took to reduce exposure to certain potential high-risk relapse factors (e.g., what people, places, events, things did they need to avoid and why?).
- Learn from peers what they did to cope and prevent relapse when they were faced with high-risk factors.

Reinforce the importance of making a commitment to long-term recovery using both professional counseling and mutual support programs.

- This provides an ongoing mechanism to identify and manage high-risk factors.
- It provides social support so that you can get help from others in recovery.

Some group members are more vulnerable to relapse than others, based on their history and severity of their illnesses and coping skills. For example:

- A group member with a long history of SUDs and multiple attempts at recovery is more vulnerable to relapse than a first-timer.
- A group member with an untreated psychiatric disorder is at increased relapse risk.
- A group member who lacks social support on a recovery network is more likely to keep problems to oneself and return to substance use.

Medication-assisted treatment can be very helpful to group members who:

- Have an opioid addiction and have not been able to sustain recovery from SUD involving these drugs with professional treatment and/or participation in mutual support programs. Methadone (Methadose®), buprenorphine (Subutex® and Suboxone®) and naltrexone (Revia®, Vivitrol®) are medications for opioid addiction.
- Have an alcohol dependence and have not be able to sustain sobriety with professional treatment or participation in mutual support programs like AA. Disulfiram (Antabuse®), naltrexone (and acamprosate (Campral®) are examples of medications for alcoholism.
- Have nicotine dependence and want to quit. Medications used for withdrawal symptoms or ongoing abstinence from nicotine include varenicline (Chantix®),

buproprion SR (Zyban®), nicotine gum, nicotine lozenges, nasal spray, puffer ("inhaler") or transdermal patch. These may be used singly or in combination to help the addicted client stop using nicotine and deal with strong cravings that often occur when a person stops using nicotine.

- While the FDA has not approved any drug for cocaine or methamphetamine addiction, research continues to try to find a drug that helps. Group members can always ask their doctor or therapist about medications for stimulant addiction.

Optional

Have members share some of their responses to Section 3 "Identifying High Risk Situations" and Section 4 "Managing High-Risk Situations" in the <u>Relapse Prevention Workbook</u>, pages 5–8. Remind them that it is not the high risk situation but the use of coping strategies that determines if a relapse is prevented.

Group Session

Setbacks: Stopping a Lapse or Relapse

Objectives

- Review the importance of being prepared to handle a setback, emergency, lapse or relapse.
- Identify benefits of continued involvement in treatment and recovery.
- Raise awareness that failure to comply with ongoing treatment increases the chance of relapse.

Discussion Points

Ask members how they define a lapse, relapse, setback or emergency as it relates to recovery from SUDs.

Group members who comply with treatment do better than those who do not. Failure to comply with treatment often contributes to relapse.

Stress the importance of keeping therapy appointments even after sobriety has been achieved and maintained for a while.

Ask group members who have failed to comply with treatment in the past, why they were non-compliant, and how this affected their recovery.

Ask group members who complied with treatment in the past to state why they complied with treatment, and how this affected their recovery.

Ask group members to identify the potential benefits of complying with treatment and recovery plans.

- Improves their chances of recovery and making positive changes.
- Decreases the risk of relapse.
- Keeps them connected with others willing to support them in recovery.
- Provides reminders of what SUDs has done to them and how recovery benefits them.

Many group members relapse so it helps to be prepared should this occur.

- Relapse can occur even if group members comply with treatment.
- However, it is less likely if treatment is complied with.

Discuss the benefits of preparing ahead of time for a setback, lapse or relapse.

- Group members are better prepared to take action quickly and early in the relapse process.

- Group members feel more hopeful about recovery if they know how to handle setbacks and potential problems.
- Damage that occurs following a lapse or relapse is limited. For example, catching a lapse may prevent a full-blown relapse.

Ask group members what they could do if they felt their treatment plan was not working or not helpful instead of dropping out of treatment.

- Talk to their treatment team about changing the plan.
- Figure out why the plan is not working.
- Talk to a sponsor.
- Talk to a peer in recovery.
- Talk to a confidante, someone whom they trust.

Ask group members to identify steps to take if they relapse to substance use.

- Stop using and get rid of booze, drugs and drug paraphernalia.
- Ask for help from a sponsor or other AA or NA friends.
- Ask for help from the treatment team.
- Seek detoxification if physical SUDs has reoccurred.
- Get back in treatment if they had dropped out before their relapse.

Review the following ideas about setbacks and emergencies:

- Preparing ahead of time allows group members to catch setbacks early, which may help prevent a full-blown relapse.
- Group members can ask for help with setbacks or emergencies from counselors, other professionals, sponsors, and friends in recovery.
- When possible, the family should be involved.
- Group members who get re-addicted physically and cannot stop alcohol or drug use will need to be detoxified under medical supervision.

Ask group members what they learned from previous lapses, relapses or setbacks.

- Causes.
- Effects.
- What they learned about relapse and recovery.
- What they learned about themselves.
- What they can do differently in the future.

Have group members complete an *Emergency Sobriety Card*. This can be written on a 3 × 5 index card and should include the following information.

- Names, phone numbers and emails of 5 supportive people.

- Names and phone numbers of organizations than can help (e.g., AA, NA, hotline).
- Reasons they would hesitate to ask for help or support.
- Benefits of asking for help or support from others.

Optional

Have members share some of their responses to Section 11 "Emergency Sobriety Card" and Section 12 "What to Do if You Relapse" in the <u>Relapse Prevention Workbook</u>, pages 22 and 23.

BUILDING A LONG-TERM RECOVERY PLAN

Objectives

- Stress the importance of a daily plan for recovery.
- Reinforce the helpfulness of participation in mutual support programs after completion of professional treatment (AA, NA and other 12-Step and non 12-Step recovery programs).
- Review the "tools" of recovery that can be used in daily life to help one maintain sobriety and continue to make positive changes.

Discussion Points

Ask group members why is important to comply with treatment and keep their appointments.

- Those who stay in treatment do better than those who drop out early.
- Treatment can help even during times of difficulty when a person is struggling or relapses.

Ask group members why they think it is important to follow a daily plan in recovery. Add examples as needed to cover these benefits:

- Helps keep group members focused and vigilant about recovery.
- Keeps them busy and focused on using positive coping strategies.
- Helps group members achieve their goals.
- Helps them spot problems or relapse warning signs early.

Discuss the possible negative consequences of dropping out of treatment early, or not following a recovery plan on a daily basis. Add examples as needed to cover the following potential problems:

- Problems are not identified or addressed promptly.
- Priorities change, and recovery can take a back seat to other priorities in life.
- Group members lose a major source of support and feedback.
- Boredom and hopelessness are more likely.
- Members can lose focus on recovery.
- Members can become too passive about recovery and actions needed to sustain recovery.
- The risk of relapse may increase.

Ask the group members to identify the benefits of ongoing participation in a recovery program following completion of treatment. Some examples include:

- Can receive continued help and support from others in recovery.
- Actively working a program of recovery reduces relapse risk.
- Involvement in recovery, especially support groups, is a constant reminder of the seriousness of SUDs and the importance of following the "disciplines" of recovery.
- Staying sober puts the recovering person in the position to continue to make positive changes in self and lifestyle, which can improve the quality of life.
- Many problems and issues emerge over time, even if one is sober from alcohol or drugs. Participation in a recovery program can make you feel better prepared to handle these issues or problems.

Discuss the length of time group members should stay involved in a mutual support recovery program such as AA or NA. This varies considerably among recovering individuals with many staying involved for years or even lifelong.

Ask members what happened to them in the past if they dropped out of treatment and/or mutual support programs early.

- How were they affected?
- Why did they drop-out?
- Did they talk about their impulse to stop treatment or recovery BEFORE making the decision to do so? If not, why not?
- What does this type of poor decision to drop out say about SUDs?

Ask the group what "tools" of recovery they can use on a regular basis. They can also state how these various recovery tools can help their ongoing recovery.

- Attending AA, NA or other mutual support meetings.
- Spending time at a recovery club or clubhouse.
- Talking with a sponsor or peers in a mutual support programs every day.
- Sharing social or recreational activities with sober friends.
- Avoiding high risk people, places, events or situations when possible.
- Using techniques to fight off thoughts of using substances, or to fight off strong cravings.
- Using positive affirmations by reminding oneself of the benefits of recovery.
- Getting physical exercise.
- Attending religious services; praying or using one's Higher Power.
- Focusing on one of the 12 Steps.
- Repeating and thinking about a recovery slogan.

- Reading recovery or inspirational literature; writing in a recovery journal or workbook.

- Participating in pleasant activities that don't involve alcohol or drugs.

- Doing something nice for someone else as a way of "giving back."

- Reviewing the plan for recovery at the beginning of each day.

- Evaluating how the day went at the end of it to review positive growth and identify problems needing attention.

- Regularly reviewing relapse warning signs to catch them early.

Ask group members why recovery should be approached "one day at a time." How can a daily inventory help?

Ask members how medications can aid recovery from alcoholism or opioid SUDs?

Optional

Have members share some of their responses to Section 9 "Building a Long-Term Recovery Plan" in the <u>Relapse Prevention Workbook</u>, pages 18–19.

LIFESTYLE BALANCING

Objectives

- Review the importance of a balanced lifestyle in preventing relapse and becoming more satisfied with life.
- Identify areas of life to check for "balance."
- Identify one area to rebalance and identify steps to take to achieve this balance.

Discussion Points

Ask group members for their view of "lifestyle balance" as it relates to recovery and relapse prevention.

- How do they define this?
- Why is lifestyle balance important in recovery?
- What areas of life should be considered?

SUDs Recovery **areas to consider:**

- Following a daily recovery program and "working" at recovery.
- Keeping appointments with SUDs counselors or doctors providing medications.
- Participating actively in mutual support programs.
- Keeping recovery a high priority in life.

Physical Health **areas to consider:**

- Getting regular dental and physical examinations.
- Complying with treatment for dental or medical problems.
- Getting sufficient sleep and relaxation.
- Following a reasonable diet.
- Stopping the use of tobacco products (especially if addicted).
- Taking medications for SUDs, psychiatric or medical problems only as prescribed.

Psychological Health **areas to consider:**

- Using active coping strategies to manage emotions or feelings.
- Challenging addictive thinking or negative thoughts.
- Coping with stresses and problems.
- Dealing with conflicts rather than avoid them.

Relationship or Interpersonal Health **areas to consider:**

- Having and using a support network.
- Staying connected to family and loved ones; involving family in recovery.

- Relating to sober people.
- Knowing who to ask for help and support.
- Knowing how to ask for help and support (learning how to reach out to others).

Spiritual Health **areas to consider:**
- Relying on God or a Higher Power for strength.
- Praying and meditating.
- Participating in religious activities.
- Participating in spiritual activities.
- Having a sense of meaning or purpose in life.

Recreational or Leisure **areas to consider:**
- Having enough substance-free leisure activities.
- Getting enjoyment from these activities.
- Feeling connected to others with whom to enjoy activities.

Work or School **areas to consider:**
- Pursuing educational or occupational (career) goals.
- Not being a workaholic at the expense of other areas of life.
- Functioning at work (being on time, doing your job).

Financial Health **areas to consider:**
- Taking care of financial obligations (self and family).
- Living within your means.
- Following a budget and managing money responsibly.
- Saving or investing in your future (and your family).

Ask group members to identify one area of their lives that is out of balance. Get several to share the details.
- What area is out of balance?
- Why? For how long?
- What steps can be taken to re-balance and change this area?

Optional
Ask members to rate the degree to which each area is in our out of balance (1=way out of balanced; 5=mid range; 10=well balanced).
- SUDs Recovery _____
- Physical Health _____
- Psychological Health _____
- Relationships and Interpersonal Health _____

- Spiritual Health _____
- Recreation/Leisure _____
- Work or School _____
- Financial Health _____

Have members share some of their answers to Section 10 "Lifestyle Balancing" of the <u>Relapse Prevention Workbook</u>, pages 20–21.

CHAPTER 6

Relapse Prevention Groups for Co-Occurring Disorders

Groups for clients with psychiatric and co-occurring disorders can also address recovery and relapse issues. These group sessions can be incorporated into inpatient, partial hospital, day programs or intensive outpatient, or ambulatory programs. Similar to relapse groups for substance use disorders and other addictions, these groups require the use of multiple interventions and formats.

Group leaders can use a variety of interventions in conducting RP group sessions. These include:

- Providing educational information (about psychiatric disorders, co-occurring disorders, drugs and alcohol, treatment, recovery and relapse)

- Facilitating group discussion and interaction among clients.

- Helping members relate to the RP concepts discussed in a personal way.

- Monitoring psychiatric symptoms (including suicidality) and substance use as well as lapses, relapses or recurrences.

- Validating issues or struggles contributing to relapse or recurrence presented by group members.

- Emphasizing positive coping strategies used by members to aid recovery and prevent relapse, or intervene early in the process.

- Encouraging continuing participation in treatment, and attendance at mutual support programs for psychiatric illness, co-occurring disorders or substance use disorders.

- Having members talk directly to each other when sharing their opinions, discussing experiences or providing feedback related to topics of RP groups or problems discussed within the group.

- Asking group members to identify and practice new coping skills or RP skills (e.g., catching early signs of psychiatric relapse, managing emotions, reaching out for help, etc.). Skills can be practiced within the group or outside the group.

GROUP FORMAT FOR OUTPATIENT SETTINGS

The following format is similar to the one in the previous chapter except it is adapted for psychiatric and co-occurring disorders. The process of orienting clients to groups is also similar to the one presented in the previous chapter. Another issue to address is preparing the client to share suicidal thoughts and concerns about self -harm should they occur during ambulatory treatment. The group leader can facilitate further suicidal assessment outside of group sessions to lower the risk of suicide.

Welcoming clients: The group leader welcomes members to the RP group session, states the topic and goals or objectives of the session. Any pertinent announcements are made to members.

Member introductions and check-in: Members state their name, psychiatric disorder(s), substance use disorder(s), current status of psychiatric symptoms, date of last use of substances, any strong cravings or "close calls" since the previous group meeting, any lapse or relapse to use, and mutual support meeting attendance since last session. Many programs have a chart on the wall listing these "check-in" items to help group members stay focused during this process. Other check-in items can be added based on type of group and length of sessions. The check-in should take 10–20 minutes so that the majority of the session is spent on the topic of the session.

Change in psychiatric symptoms or substance use: If a group member's psychiatric condition is worsening, or has used substances since the last session the group may briefly process the event and discuss a plan to reduce relapse risk or suicide risk. Any member with a significant worsening of symptoms may be seen between or after group sessions to determine if a higher level of care is needed due to changes in symptoms.

Handouts or assignments: Recovery and relapse prevention handouts from a workbook, journal or other source or behavioral assignments are briefly reviewed if assigned at the previous session. Since interactive recovery tasks take time, it is most efficient to assign these tasks prior to the RP group session so members can reflect upon the topic, and complete interactive tasks aimed at getting them to relate to the RP material. If members fail to complete an assignment this should be discussed in terms of the implications for recovery or relapse.

Group topic introduction: The group leader introduces the RP topic and reviews the major points noted on the outline for the specific topic. Questions and interactive explorations are used throughout the session. Members are asked to share their reactions to the material presented. They are encouraged to discuss how the RP topic relates to their personal situations. Group members are encouraged to interact and offer feedback to one another when appropriate. Most of the session is spent on an interactive discussion of the material related to the group topic. This part of the group should last 45–60 minutes in 90-minute sessions. If groups are 60 minutes, this section should last 40–45 minutes. Make sure sufficient time is spent on "coping strategies" so that all or most of session is not spent only on the problems or struggles presented by clients relevant to the topic.

Review of homework (optional): In small groups (less than 10 members) members can briefly share answers to questions on the handouts provided if homework was assigned. This is optional as some groups can discuss the questions without using written handouts. The group leader has to control the flow of dialogue so that members do not get into lengthy discussions when they share their answers to a specific question. Some members, for example, want to give extensive details about any issue they discuss whether it is a personal craving, a relapse warning sign, or any issue related to recovery or relapse.

Group ending: In the final 10–15 minutes of the group session, members state one thing they learned (information, idea, coping strategy) from the RP group and state their plans for recovery until the next session. Clients are encouraged to attend mutual support meetings, get and use a sponsor, get phone numbers from other AA, NA, DRA members, and actually call these members.

RP assignment (optional): Assignments related to the next session's topic can be given to group members with a brief explanation as to what is required. These can be from a written guide (e.g., a workbook or recovery journal), a written handout (e.g., a sheet of paper with a few questions related to the next group session's topic) or a behavioral task (e.g., members are asked to talk to at least 1 or 2 other people in a mutual support program to find out how they managed upsetting emotions, suicidal thoughts or strong cravings).

Serenity Prayer (optional): The group joins hands and recites the Serenity Prayer aloud to end the session.

GROUP FORMAT IN INPATIENT SETTINGS

Groups can be offered on inpatient units and should be conducted in an interactive manner in which clients are engaged to share personal experiences related to the information presented. Educational videos, interactive presentations and guest presenters can be used (e.g., with the latter, peers in recovery can share their experiences in working a recovery plan to deal with their co-occurring disorders).

Inpatient groups are usually 45–60 minutes so the format of the topic has to be adjusted to account for less group time. After a review of the group topic, the leader can ask each member to state one thing they learned that stood out to them or that they see as a "take home" message about relapse and recovery.

The strategies presented in the previous chapter (brief lectures, stories, guest speakers, educational videos, the use of written handouts or workbooks, recovery readings, behavioral rehearsals, monodramas, creative media, and the use of PowerPoint slides) can be incorporated into group sessions.

8 STRUCTURED RP GROUPS

Group topics can be adapted to the treatment setting and population. Some of the content is very similar to that for RP groups for substance use disorders, except that the strategies are adapted to psychiatric disorders. Following is a brief review of group sessions.

Recovery from psychiatric or co-occurring disorders (CODs). This provides an overview of recovery from psychiatric illness or CODs, and the areas clients should consider in developing their recovery plans as a way to reduce relapse risk.

Managing early relapse warning signs. Clients learn illness specific and other common warning signs of relapse or recurrence. Focus is also on taking action to reduce the likelihood that a full blown recurrence will occur.

Identifying and managing relapse risk factors in psychiatric illness. Common risk factors are reviewed so that clients become more aware of risks they may face. These risk factors may relate to the psychiatric disorder(s), substance use, adherence to treatment, or the use (or non-use) of coping strategies.

Establishing a recovery support system. This session focuses on the importance of, and benefits of, social support in recovery. Clients are asked to identify people, organizations that support recovery, reasons it may be hard to reach out for help and support from others, and how to ask for help.

Managing emotions or moods. Members learn to identify emotions or moods, and understand what contributes to these. Most importantly, the group focuses on strategies to manage and decrease negative emotions, and increase positive emotions.

Healthy leisure activities and lifestyle change. This focuses on the need to build structure into daily life and engage in pleasant and healthy activities.

Addressing alcohol or drug use. Members learn how substances can affect their psychiatric illness, as well as what they can do to address a co-existing substance disorder.

Setbacks and stopping a psychiatric relapse. The focus of this session is to help the members prepare for potential relapses or other emergencies or setbacks.

Group Session

RECOVERY FROM PSYCHIATRIC OR CO-OCCURRING DISORDERS

Objectives

- Define recovery as a process of managing the disorders and making changes.
- Review domains of recovery: physical, psychological, family, social, interpersonal, spiritual.
- Review common resistances or roadblocks to recovery.
- Review potential benefits of recovery.

Discussion Points

Ask clients to define recovery from psychiatric or co-occurring disorders and to identify resources needed to aid their recovery (professional, mutual support, other resources).

Discuss the differences between "treatment" and "recovery."

- Treatment involves professional care in an inpatient, residential and/or ambulatory mental health/co-occurring disorders program.
- Counseling/therapy, medications or a combination may be needed, depending on your disorders, their severity and impact on your life.
- Treatment helps members engage in recovery, and learn skills to manage the disorders and problems. Recovery is the work done to manage your disorders and change your life.
- Other services may also help you in your recovery (e.g., case management, vocational counseling or training).

Ask clients how continued substance use can impact on recovery from a psychiatric illness.

- Can lower your motivation to change or work a program of recovery.
- Can cause you to feel bad (guilty, ashamed), which can lead to negative thinking.
- Can make you rely on substances to feel good temporarily.
- Can interfere with psychiatric medication.

Ask clients to identify the different components or domains of recovery.

- *Physical*: take medication, abstain from alcohol, illicit and non-prescribed drugs, exercise, eat a healthy diet, get adequate sleep, take care of medical and dental problems, deal with pain, and manage cravings for drugs or alcohol.
- *Psychological/emotional*: accept the psychiatric disorder and develop motivation to change, manage symptoms of illness, change thinking, manage emotions and

moods, and cope with stresses and problems without relying on alcohol or other drugs.

- *Family*: review the effects of illness on the family and individuals, involve the family in treatment and recovery, improve relationships, and make amends.
- *Social/interpersonal*: review the impact of disorders on work or relationships, address problems with others, develop a recovery network, and reach out for help and support.
- *Spiritual*: this may involve relying on a Higher Power for help and strength, developing a sense of purpose and meaning in life, taking other steps to improve one's faith or "inner, spiritual life," attending services, praying, meditating or reading spiritual or religious literature.

Ask clients to identify barriers or roadblocks to recovery (things that can interfere with getting involved and working a recovery program).

- *Attitude and motivation* roadblocks such as periods of low motivation, difficulty accepting the disorder(s) and need for help, not caring about recovery, or not wanting to do the work required to make positive changes in oneself.
- *Personality* roadblocks such as not being open to letting others help and support you, being stubborn, self-centered, or too negative and angry.
- *Relationship* roadblocks such as close connections with, or living with, people who mistreat you, do not support your recovery, or influence you to use drugs or alcohol. Wanting to recover alone without the help or support of other people.
- *Lifestyle* roadblocks such as limited structure in one's days or weeks, lack of engagement in meaningful activities, not having goals or a direction in life, or having an unstable living environment.
- *Treatment or recovery participation* roadblocks such as cutting down or missing counseling sessions or mutual support program meetings, not taking medications as prescribed, mixing alcohol or drugs with psychiatric medications, signing out of the hospital against medical advice, dropping out of treatment early, or expecting others to solve your problems.

Ask clients to identify the actual or potential advantages or benefits to recovery. These can relate to improvements in any area that improves the quality of life:

- Physical, mental or emotional, social, interpersonal, spiritual, or financial health.
- Cognitive (clearer thinking or better problem solving ability).
- Family or social relationships; or ability to attend school or work.

Discuss the advantages of ongoing involvement in recovery and what it involves.

- Addressing both disorders in recovery.
- Patience, discipline, a specific plan, and hard work.
- Bouncing back from setbacks or problems.

Ask members to identify and discuss coping strategies to deal with periods of low motivation and/or to continue their recovery. Focus on the need to use positive coping strategies.

- Accepting responsibility for recovery and making changes in self and life.
- Identifying specific changes to make in different domains of recovery.
- Identifying and overcoming low motivation or roadblocks to recovery.
- Acknowledging the potential and actual benefits of long-term recovery.
- Engaging in mutual support programs based on problems, needs and interests.
- Reading inspirational literature or recovery literature.
- Maintaining recovery disciplines even in the face of declining motivation.

Discuss how recovery is best viewed as a *"we" process* in which you use the support of others, especially others who are actively working a program of recovery.

Ask clients to identify one change they would like to make in recovery, and have each state or write down several steps to take to make this change.

MANAGING EARLY RELAPSE WARNING SIGNS

Objectives

- Teach group members that warning signs precede relapse to a psychiatric disorder.
- Review common warning signs associated with relapse related to the specific psychiatric disorder (mood, anxiety, psychotic, other).
- Review subtle warning signs that may be unique to each individual.
- Identify strategies to manage early relapse warning signs.
- For those who have had one or more relapses, teach them to use this as a learning experience to help their future recovery.

Discussion Points

Ask group members to define relapse as it relates to their psychiatric disorders. State that the term "recurrence" is usually used to refer to a new episode (relapse) of psychiatric illness.

Ask group members who have relapsed for examples of early warning signs from past experiences. Add additional examples as needed and state that warning signs will fall in the following categories: cognitive, emotional, behavioral, or physical.

- *Symptoms of a specific psychiatric disorder*: cognitive, emotional, behavioral, or physical.
- *Changes in thinking*: "I don't need recovery, it's not worth the effort, I don't need medications anymore;" increase in severity of compulsions to drink or use drugs.
- *Changes in mood*: Significant increase in anger, anxiety, boredom, or depression.
- *Changes in health habits or daily routines*: Not taking care of personal hygiene or changes in daily habits or rituals.
- *Changes in behavior*: Stopping or cutting down on treatment sessions, medications, or support group meetings without prior discussion with a professional or sponsor; reducing social interactions or activities; or reduced use of the "tools of recovery."

Emphasize the importance of catching relapse warning signs early.

- The earlier that group members intervene, the less likely that relapse will occur.
- Ignoring warning signs is not a good strategy as they must be dealt with.

Discuss the importance of not keeping warning signs a secret as things can build up and end in a relapse. Failure to identify or deal with relapse warning signs invites problems.

Discuss the difference between common and individual or personal warning signs. Elicit examples from each category.

- Common warning signs include cutting down or stopping mutual support meetings, counseling or medication-assisted treatment for SUDs.

- Individual or personal warning signs may include an increase in dishonesty or depression during the holidays.

Ask group members to identify strategies to manage relapse warning signs. Their specific examples should fall into the following broad categories:

- *Cognitive:* Changing thoughts and beliefs (e.g., challenging the thought, "I can't have fun without alcohol or drugs" or, "Just because I didn't get the job I wanted doesn't mean I have to get depressed and give up").

- *Behavioral:* Changing a behavior (e.g., resuming regular meeting attendance when one identifies cutting back as a warning sign; taking medications as prescribed after one identifies cutting down or stopping without first discussing this with a doctor or therapist).

- *Interpersonal:* Seeking help and support from others in AA or NA (e.g., talking with others about ways to manage warning signs).

Use this information to emphasize the importance of *being aware of warning signs* and having a plan to manage them.

Discuss the importance of *seeking support from others* to manage warning signs (e.g., AA or NA friends and sponsors, counselor, friends, family, etc.).

Discuss the importance of *learning from past experiences* with lapse or relapse. If a group member has had multiple relapses following periods of recovery, the group leader can suggest that she review the most recent ones to see if there are any patterns to her behavior that indicate a relapse was likely to happen. Focus should also be on coming up with strategies to manage past warning signs that may occur in the future.

Optional

Have members share some of their responses to Section 5 "Red Flags: Warning Signs of Relapse (pp. 23-26)," and Section 6 "Managing Relapse Warning Signs (pp. 27-29)" in Relapse Prevention in Psychiatric Illness.

IDENTIFYING AND MANAGING RELAPSE RISK FACTORS IN PSYCHIATRIC ILLNESS

Objectives

- Review factors that increase the risk of relapse to either type of disorder and label these as "high risk."
- Teach group members that relapse risk factors fall into different categories, but it is usually a combination of factors, rather than just one, that leads to relapse.
- Emphasize the importance of learning and using active coping skills to manage relapse risk factors.

Discussion Points

Relapse is common with co-occurring disorders.

- The term "recurrence" is used for psychiatric disorders and refers to a new episode of illness after a period of stable recovery (or remission).
- For substance use disorders, "relapse" refers to returning to the use of alcohol or drugs after a period of sobriety.
- Relapse is also common with chronic or recurrent medical disorders.
- Relapse does not mean failure; it means the person has to learn different ways to manage the co-occurring disorders.
- Many factors can be high risk and increase a person's vulnerability to relapse. These are referred to as "high-risk" factors
- These factors vary among individuals in recovery
- What is high-risk for one person may not be high-risk for another person.

Ask group members to identify high-risk relapse factors for their co-occurring disorders.

- While there may be similarities between high risk relapse factors for substance use and psychiatric disorders, there are differences as well.
- For individuals with SUDs, high risk factors are situations in which they used alcohol or drugs in the past.
- For individuals with psychiatric disorders, high risk factors can include the use of alcohol or other drugs in addition to other factors.
- These factors can relate to the psychiatric disorder, lifestyle or coping mechanisms of the individual in recovery.

As group members share examples of high-risk factors, classify them in categories such as: internal (thoughts or emotions/moods), external (relationships, support system), and lifestyle (habits, structure in life, daily routines). Specific examples include:

- Negative, pessimistic or faulty thinking in which the person expects the worst outcome of a situation, looks for the negative in life, focuses more on symptoms and problems than solutions and recovery, or has an increase in confusion, disorganized or bizarre thoughts, or thoughts related to harming self or others.

- Negative emotional states or moods, which become more frequent and/or intense. These could relate to anger, anxiety, boredom, depression, loneliness, guilt or shame.

- Social pressures to use alcohol or drugs or stop taking psychiatric medications.

- Relationship factors such a serious problems with others, a significant loss that is hard to handle, isolating self from others, limited or no social support, or involvement in relationships in which others are too critical, hostile or psychologically or physically abusive.

- Lifestyle factors such as lack of goals, direction, structure or regularity in life, excessive stress, medical problems or changes in health status, major life changes or negative events, or lack of coping skills to manage the co-occurring disorders.

- The use of alcohol or drugs can be a risk factor for relapse to the psychiatric disorder.

- Strong urges, cravings, desires or obsessions can be a risk factor for relapse to a substance use disorder.

In addition to identifying high-risk relapse factors, group members also need to *learn and actively use coping skills to* manage these factors effectively.

- Ask them why they think coping skills are necessary to reduce relapse risk.

- And, ask for examples of coping skills that have helped them in the past deal with either of their disorders.

- Try to solicit a variety of cognitive and behavioral coping skills.

- Include the use of medications and support networks as strategies to help cope with certain high risk situations and to facilitate recovery.

Ask clients what they can do if they try a specific coping strategy but it does not work with a high-risk situation.

- Emphasize the need for flexibility and having multiple coping strategies as no one strategy can work all the time.

- Ask what they have learned from peers on how they deal with high-risk relapse factors.

Reinforce the need to make a commitment to long-term recovery using both professional counseling and mutual support programs.

- This provides an ongoing mechanism to identify and manage high-risk factors.
- It provides social support, which allows group members to receive help and support from others, especially peers in recovery.

Some group members are more vulnerable to relapse than others, based on their history and severity of their illnesses and coping skills. For example:

- A group member with a long history of SUDs and multiple attempts at recovery is more vulnerable to relapse than a first-timer.
- A group member with an untreated psychiatric disorder is at increased relapse risk.
- A group member with a recurrent or chronic type of psychiatric disorder may be
  at increased risk of relapse due to the nature of the disorder(s).
- A group member who lacks social support or a recovery network is more likely to keep problems to oneself and return to substance use or feel increasing depressed.

Medication-assisted treatment can be very helpful to group members who have an addiction to substances like alcohol, opioids or nicotine.

- Methadone (Methadose®), buprenorphine (Subutex® and Suboxone®) and naltrexone (Revia®, Vivitrol®) are medications for opioid SUDs.
- Disulfiram (Antabuse®), naltrexone (ReVia or) and acamprosate (Campral®) are medications for alcoholism.
- Varenicline (Chantix®), buproprion SR (Zyban®), nicotine gum, nicotine lozenges, nasal spray, puffer ("inhaler") or transdermal patches can be used for nicotine addiction.
- Medications are used for other substance addictions, but are not yet approved by the FDA.

Medications can also be used to treat more severe symptoms of psychiatric illness (acute or chronic symptoms), or a return of symptoms after a period of remission. These include medications for:

- Mood disorders such as bipolar illness or depression.
- All types of anxiety disorders.
- PTSD and trauma.
- Psychotic disorders such as schizophrenia.
- Attention deficit disorder.

- Other psychiatric disorders (depends on the diagnosis, specific symptoms, and the severity of these symptoms).

Other issues to discuss relevant to medications include the following:

- Medications for psychiatric disorders are not equally effective for all people who use them.

- Medications can either lead to a remission of symptoms or a reduction in the severity of symptoms. Some symptoms may never go away totally (they are called persistent or chronic symptoms).

- Taking medications regularly AND only as prescribed are important to get the maximum benefit.

- A desire to stop taking meds should always be discussed first with a doctor or therapist since premature cessation of medications often contributes to psychiatric relapse.

- Medications are best used with therapy, counseling and other types of programs that help deal with co-occurring disorders.

- Wanting more or a different medication if symptoms change or worsen is not always the best strategy to use. However, there may be times when a change in medications is needed.

- Avoiding mixing medications with alcohol, street drugs or other non-prescribed drugs increases the odds of recovery.

ESTABLISHING A RECOVERY SUPPORT SYSTEM

Objectives

- Define social support and its importance in recovery.
- Identify the benefits of having a recovery support system.
- Identify supportive people and organizations to include in a recovery support system.
- Identify reasons why it may be difficult to ask others for help or support.
- Identify ways to approach others and ask for help or support.

Discussion Points

Ask group members to define social support, and state why it is so important in ongoing recovery from co-occurring disorders.

Many mutual support programs exist to aid recovery and reduce relapse risk. All of these programs have "tools" to help the person recover.

Many people find the 12 Step fellowship of AA, NA, and CA helps their ongoing recovery.

- Meetings, sponsors, friendships with peers in recovery, the 12 Steps, slogans and recovery literature are all "tools" of 12-Step recovery that can help you stay sober and make positive changes over time.
- Others find non 12-Step programs helpful in their recovery (Women for Sobriety, SMART Recovery, Rational Recovery, etc).

In addition, other people and organizations can also provide you with help and support. These people do not have to be associated with a recovery program.

Then ask group members to give examples of people they might ask for help and support.

- Specific family members
- Specific friends
- A boss or coworker
- A neighbor
- A priest, minister or rabbi
- Other people?

Ask members of the group to give examples of organizations or groups that can play an important role in their efforts to stay sober and change their lifestyles.

- Church or synagogue
- Sports team

- Club that involves a specific interest
- Volunteer organizations

Ask group members to give examples of how other people and organizations can play a role in their recovery.

- Other people can listen to their problems or concerns.
- Other people can be asked for specific help with a problem or situation.
- Other people can participate in mutually-satisfying activities or events that do not evolve around alcohol or drug use (e.g., share a hobby, go to a movie together, etc.).
- Organizations can give a sense of belonging.
- Organizations can offer opportunities for social interaction, a chance to develop new friendships or interests, or a chance to learn new skills.
- Church-related organizations can provide an opportunity for spiritual growth.
- Other?

Ask group members to give examples of people they <u>should not ask for help</u> or support.

- Others who still get drunk or high and have no interest in supporting them in recovery.
- People who are angry at the recovering person and may still be holding a grudge.
- People who don't want the recovering person to succeed at getting or staying sober.
- Other?

Ask the group to give reasons why it is difficult to reach out and seek help or support from others.

- Fear of rejection.
- Feeling unworthy to be helped by others.
- Don't know how to be assertive and make requests to other people.
- Feeling shy and awkward.
- Embarrassed to have to ask another for something.
- Fear of sounding inadequate.
- Hard to trust others and open up.

Ask members to share ideas on how to "reach out" to others for help and support.

- Make a list of people that they trust and feel they can rely on.
- Choose one or two to start with in terms of asking for help or support.
- Talk with them about recovery and the need for their support.

- Communicate regularly, not just in times of trouble.
- Talk face-to-face, by phone, email or text messaging.
- Take a risk and open up to others.
- Also, show an interest in their lives.

Optional

Create role plays in which a member: a) asks for help and support from a friend, family member or confidante; or b) asks a member of AA or NA to be a sponsor.

- Then, discuss what the experience was like.
- What were the barriers to reaching out for help and support?
- Who are the people to reach out for to get help and support in recovery?
- What are ways to reach out (i.e., what can the members say?).

MANAGING EMOTIONS OR MOODS

Objectives

- Define the three components of an emotion or mood: feelings, thoughts and behaviors.
- Identify connections between emotions and relapse.
- Review causes and effects of emotion.
- Review strategies to manage or cope with anger from other people.

Discussion Points

Define emotions and mood and their importance in life.

- An emotion is a subjective feeling such as sadness or anxiety.
- A mood is a prolonged emotion such as sadness becoming depression.
- Discuss how emotions or moods involve feelings, thoughts, and behaviors.
- Both positive and negative emotions are an important part of life.
- Ask for examples of how anger and anxiety can be either negative or positive.
- Emotions can become a problem if they are too intense, extreme, chronic and overwhelming.
- Understanding and recognizing different emotions enables the person to be better equipped to deal with emotions, especially distressing ones.

Ask members to share examples of specific emotions or moods they have experienced. Identify which ones they believe they need to better manage in their recovery. Make a list that includes:

- Anxiety, worry, fear
- Boredom, emptiness
- Depression, sadness, grief
- Guilt, shame, embarrassment
- Loneliness
- Other negative emotions or moods

Discuss factors that cause or contribute to emotions or moods. Many factors can contribute to a specific emotion. These include:

- Physical factors: hormones, neurotransmitters in the brain, pain, and effects of medical conditions or medications.
- Alcohol or drugs: even small amounts of a substance can impact on any number of emotions.

- Personality: some people are more prone to anger, anxiety, depression or negativity than others.
- Thinking and beliefs about self and the world: negative thoughts can contribute to anxiety or depression, or other negative emotions.
- Experiences in life and stress: events and situations a person encounters in life impact on emotions and moods. For example, a traumatic event can lead to feeling sad or depressed.
- Actions or behaviors: how a person acts can affect how they feel. For example, if a person loses a job, gets angry and does nothing, the anger may increase or depression may be experienced.
- Relationships with others: having a confidant and caring, supportive people in life can help protect against negative emotions or moods, especially if these are shared with others in an appropriate manner.
- Other factors: these include accomplishment and opportunities.

Discuss effects of emotions not managed by group members.

- Avoiding them may lead to these building up on the inside. Once a certain point is reached, the person may feel overwhelmed by the emotions.
- Unhealthy ways also include acting out and threatening or hurting others physically or verbally; hurting oneself; being passive; drinking or using drugs; and acting in passive-aggressive ways.
- Poorly managed emotions can affect physical health, relationships with others and ability to reach goals or succeed in life.

Ask group members to give examples of how they identify their specific emotions or moods.

- These can show in physical symptoms such as tension, anxiety or headaches.
- These can show in thinking such as admitting to self that a certain emotion is being experienced.
- These can show in behaviors or how a person acts. For example, anger can be shown in hostile, aggressive ways. Or, anger can be shown in passive aggressive behaviors such as criticizing a person behind their back, not "remembering" an important occasion such as a birthday or anniversary.

Discuss the connection between emotions and relapse.

- Negative emotions that are not managed properly can increase the risk of relapse to alcohol or drug use after a period of recovery.
- Negative emotions can build up and contribute to psychiatric symptoms such as increased thoughts of suicide or actually making an attempt; or, sadness that builds up can contribute to an episode of clinical depression.

Ask members to identify positive emotions they believe are important.

- Compassion
- Gratitude
- Hope
- Forgiveness
- Love
- Others

Discuss the benefits of increasing positive emotions.

- Improved mental health
- Improved physical health
- Better relationships
- Greater satisfaction in recovery
- Better quality of life

Review emotional management strategies.

- Recognition, or being aware of emotions or moods. Know your high-risk emotional states or moods.
- Understand what causes an emotion or mood state. Address problems that contribute to a specific emotion or mood.
- Evaluate the effects of strategies used (or not used) to handle emotions.
- Identify and use new coping strategies.
- Practice these ahead of time if needed.
- Change strategies that do not work; keep those that do work.
- Focus on decreasing negative emotions in daily life.
- Focus on increasing positive emotions in daily life (gratitude, forgiveness, love and others). Discuss benefits of positive emotions.

HEALTHY LEISURE ACTIVITIES AND LIFESTYLE CHANGE

Objectives

- Identify ways that boredom affects recovery and can impact on relapse.
- Identify sources of boredom and "high-risk" times.
- Review the importance of structure and routine in daily life.
- Review strategies to manage boredom and engage in substance-free social activities.

Discussion Points

Ask group members to identify and discuss how boredom affects recovery. Problems associated with boredom include:

- Relapse to alcohol or drug use.
- Feeling depressed.
- Getting involved in activities that may temporarily reduce boredom but create other problems.
- Getting involved with people you used substances with in the past and who now may pose a threat to your recovery.
- Making major decisions that are not well thought out and are based on feeling bored (e.g., ending important relationships or quitting a job without having another job).

Discuss how group members feel about living without alcohol or drugs, or partying.

- They may miss the company of people they used or got high with.
- They may miss the action of bars or parties.
- They may feel nothing can replace the high feeling produced by alcohol or drug use.
- They may even feel "empty" at first, like life has little meaning or direction.

Identify and list leisure activities given up due to the disorders.

- Why did they give up certain activities?
- Which of these do they miss the most?
- Which of these could be regained?

Identify drug-free or non-substance-related activities or situations that bring pleasure or enjoyment, or are fun. Discuss how or why these activities bring pleasure, enjoyment or meaning.

- Social events
- Interpersonal relationships
- Athletic
- Creative
- Artistic
- Musical
- Spiritual
- Collecting
- Fixing or repairing Other

Identify and discuss the benefits of having structure in daily life.

- Reduces the chances of engaging in high-risk situations causing relapse.
- Gives a sense of direction and purpose.
- Forces you to focus on goals and methods to achieve these goals.
- Facilitates accountability with your time.

Review practical coping strategies to reduce boredom.

- Recognize boredom, high-risk times for it and reasons for it.
- Regain "lost" activities that are not substance-related.
- Develop new leisure interests or hobbies.
- Learn to appreciate the simple pleasures in life.
- Build fun or pleasant activities into day-to-day life.
- Change thoughts and beliefs about boredom.
- Change thoughts and beliefs about involvement in drug-free activities.
- Evaluate relationship or job boredom before making major life changes.
- Deal with persistent feelings of boredom.
- Participate in recovery support groups or recovery clubs.

Discuss the issue of "emptiness" and "joylessness" associated with giving up substances, and how this contributes to both boredom and an inability to experience pleasure in normal activities.

Optional

Have group members complete a daily or weekly activities schedule to get them to practice building structure and activities into their daily lives.

Create role plays in which a client asks another person (family member or friend) to participate in a non-substance leisure activity. A variation of this is to have a client role play a situation in which he is invited to participate in a leisure activity that could threaten his sobriety (e.g., event where alcohol flows freely or others will be using drugs).

Have members share some of their responses to Section 7 "Managing Boredom and Using Leisure Time" in the Relapse Prevention Workbook, pages 14–15. Remind them to use some of the strategies to manage boredom listed on page 15.

<u>Group Session</u>

ADDRESSING ALCOHOL OR DRUG USE

Objectives

- Review substances used and reasons for using.
- Identify how these substances affect psychiatric symptoms.
- Identify effects of substance use and substance use disorders on all areas of health and functioning.
- Review a continuum of substance problems.
- Review treatments for substance use disorders.
- Review recovery from substance use disorders and mutual support programs.

Discussion Points

Ask group members what substances they have used.

- The most common substances used among individuals with psychiatric illness are nicotine, alcohol, cannabis (marijuana), stimulants (cocaine, methamphetamine, medications used for weight control or attention deficit disorder), opioids (pain pills or narcotics, heroin), and medications used for anxiety or sleep (benzodiazepines).
- Other substance used include hallucinogens, club drugs (ketamine, GHB, others), inhalants, K2 or spice (synthetic marijuana), phencyclidine (PCP) and many others.

Ask members why they drink alcohol or use other substances and factors that cause a substance use disorder (SUD).

- Reasons for using.
- Causes of a SUD.
- Discuss how SUDs run in families, similar to medical or psychiatric disorders.

Identify effects of substances on psychiatric symptoms or recovery from a psychiatric disorder.

- Moods or emotions.
- Cognitive symptoms or thinking.
- Behaviors.
- Physical symptoms.

Ask group members for examples of other effects of their substance use or SUD on:

- Physical, dental or sexual health
- Emotional or psychological health

- Family
- Relationships
- Social or leisure activities
- Work or school
- Legal
- Financial
- Spiritual

Review a continuum of substance use from no problem to a SUD.

- No use, mild use, moderate use, heavy use.
- Define heavy use of alcohol for men and women.
- Review substance use disorders: mild, moderate, severe.
- Addiction as a severe SUD.
- Review symptoms of a SUD.

Review treatment programs and therapies for SUDs

- Residential or hospital based programs.
- Partial hospital or intensive outpatient programs.
- Outpatient or continuing care programs.
- Specialty programs for narcotic or opioid addiction (therapy and medications).
- Counseling or therapy.
- Medication-assisted therapies for nicotine, alcohol or opioid dependence.
- Goals of treatment include: help you learn about and engage in recovery, and learn skills to manage your disorders and problems.
- Other services may be recommended by your treatment team (e.g., case management, vocational counseling or training, housing, etc).

Ask clients to define recovery and identify the different domains of recovery.

- Recovery is the process of managing the disorders.
- This involves making changes in oneself and lifestyle.
- If time permits, have members give examples of one change they want to make as well as steps to achieve this change.

Review experiences in mutual support programs (MSPs) and ways they can aid recovery

- Ask for both negative and positive experiences in MSPs.
- Types of 12- step programs attended: AA, NA, other 12-step.

- Types of non-12 step programs attended: women for sobriety, alcoholics victorious, and others.
- Support programs for mental health or dual disorders.
- Recovery clubs.
- Internet chat rooms on recovery.
- Discuss goals for MSPs.
- Discuss potential benefits of MSPs.

SETBACKS & STOPPING A PSYCHIATRIC RELAPSE

Objectives

- Review the importance of being prepared to handle a setback, emergency, lapse, relapse or recurrence.
- Identify benefits of continued involvement in treatment and recovery.
- Raise awareness that failure to comply with ongoing treatment increases the chance of relapse.

Discussion Points

Ask members how they define a lapse, relapse, recurrence, setback or emergency as it relates to recovery.

Group members who comply with treatment do better than those who do not. Failure to comply with treatment often contributes to relapse.

Stress the importance of keeping therapy appointments even after sobriety or psychiatrical stability has been achieved and maintained for a while.

Ask group members who have failed to comply with treatment in the past why they were non-compliant and how this affected their recovery.

Ask group members who complied with treatment in the past to state why they complied with treatment, and how this affected their recovery.

Ask group members to identify the potential benefits of complying with treatment and recovery plans.

- Improves their chances of recovery and making positive changes.
- Decreases the risk of relapse.
- Keeps them connected with others willing to support them in recovery.
- Provides reminders of what SUDs has done to them and how recovery benefits them.

Group members frequently relapse so it helps to be prepared should this occur.

- Relapse can occur even if group members comply with treatment.
- However, it is less likely if treatment is complied with.

Discuss the benefits of preparing ahead of time for a setback.

- Group members are better prepared to take action quickly and early in the relapse process.
- Group members feel more hopeful about recovery if they know how to handle setbacks and potential problems.

- Damage that occurs following a lapse or relapse is limited. For example, catching a lapse may prevent a full-blown relapse.

Ask group members what they could do if they felt their treatment plan was not working or not helpful instead of dropping out of treatment.

- Talk to their treatment team about changing the plan.
- Figure out why the plan is not working.
- Talk to a sponsor.
- Talk to a peer in recovery.
- Talk to a confidante, someone who they trust.

Ask group members to identify steps to take if they relapse to substance use, or have a recurrence of psychiatric illness following a period of recovery.

- Stop using and get rid of booze, drugs and drug paraphernalia.
- Ask for help from a sponsor or other AA or NA friends.
- Ask for help from the treatment team.
- Seek detoxification if physical addiction has reoccurred.
- Get back in treatment if they had dropped out before their relapse.
- Resume taking psychiatric medications if these were stopped.

Review the following ideas about setbacks and emergencies:

- Preparing ahead of time allows group members to catch setbacks early, which may help prevent a full-blown relapse.
- Group members can ask for help with setbacks or emergencies from counselors, other professionals, sponsors, and friends in recovery.
- When possible, the family should be involved.
- Group members who get re-addicted physically and cannot stop alcohol or drug use will need to be detoxified under medical supervision.
- Go to a psychiatric hospital emergency room if a symptoms of psychiatric illness become severe, debilitating and impair the ability to take care of oneself.
- If you have a suicide plan or are worried you may act on suicidal feelings, seek immediate help at a psychiatric hospital or other hospital emergency room, call a crisis or suicide hotline or program, or call a professional involved in your outpatient care (psychiatrist, therapist, other).

Ask group members what they learned from previous lapses, relapses or setbacks.

- Causes.
- Effects.
- What they learned about relapse and recovery.

- What they learned about themselves.
- What they can do differently in the future.

Have group members complete an Emergency Card. This can be written on a 3 x 5 index card or on their phones and include:
- Names, phone numbers and emails of 5 supportive people.
- Names and phone numbers of organizations that can help (AA, NA, DRA, suicide or crisis hotlines or programs).
- Reasons they would hesitate to ask for help or support.
- Benefits of asking for help or support from others.

Optional

Have members share some of their responses to Section 11, "Emergency Sobriety Card" and Section 12, "What to Do if You Relapse" in the <u>Relapse Prevention Workbook</u>, pages 22 and 23. Also, have members share responses to Section 12, page 29, "Managing Relapse Warning Signs" in <u>Relapse Prevention for Psychiatric Illness</u>.

CHAPTER 7

Problem Solving or Therapy Groups

Therapy or problem solving groups provide clients an opportunity to discuss specific issues, concerns or problems that impact on their recovery and their lives. Specific issues discussed may relate to any domain of life: physical, psychological, social, family, interpersonal, spiritual, or other. Therapy groups allow members to discuss issues in greater detail than structured recovery groups, which can lead to gaining personal insight and making decisions to change something specific. Any issue affecting recovery or relapse can be addressed in these groups.

OBJECTIVES OF GROUPS

These groups are used in many structured residential and ambulatory treatment programs. Programs that offer substantial numbers of groups per week can incorporate therapy groups on a daily basis or several times per week. This provides ample opportunity for clients to explore issues affecting recovery and relapse.

The objectives of problem solving or therapy groups in treatment are to:

- Help clients learn to prioritize problems and work together on these as a group.
- Support clients dealing with difficulties faced in their recovery.
- Encourage personal responsibility for ongoing recovery and relapse prevention.
- Facilitate clients' self-disclosure of feelings, thoughts, struggles and problems.
- Help members learn to give and receive support from peers.
- Help members identify and use positive coping strategies to address problems.
- Help members learn relapse prevention coping strategies (behavioral and cognitive).
- Assist clients in learning how to give and receive constructive feedback.

GROUP FORMAT

Following is one way in which to structure and conduct these types of groups. This format can be changed depending on whether the group is held weekly or is one of many types of groups clients are participating in as part of a rehabilitation or intensive outpatient program.

1. When the group meeting starts, members introduce themselves, share the type of SUD they are getting help with, and state their dates of last use (this includes use of any type

135

of drug or alcohol). Members are encouraged to briefly discuss how they are doing, any cravings, temptations, or "close calls" they have experienced since the previous group meeting. If this is a daily therapy group in a rehab or intensive outpatient program, discussions can focus on current problems of clients.

2. Members who have a psychiatric disorder can state the type of disorder(s) they have and any significant change in symptoms, or whether they feel suicidal.

3. If someone has used substances since the last session, the member can briefly process the event and develop a plan to prevent further relapse.

4. Members are encouraged to identify current problems in life or concerns about recovery that could impact on relapse. Since not all members will have a chance to discuss their individual problems, the group leader should help the members prioritize problems to be explored. Problems can be listed on a chalkboard or flip chart before deciding which ones to discuss in the group session.

5. In the final 10–15 minutes of a weekly therapy group, members are asked to state their plans for the next week in an effort to help them structure their time. In addition, they are encouraged to state their plans to attend mutual support meetings.

PROBLEMS DISCUSSED IN PROBLEM SOLVING OR THERAPY GROUPS

Any of the recovery issues and problems discussed in structured recovery or RP groups may be explored in therapy or problem solving groups. The most common issues discussed are those related to staying free from alcohol or other drug use, relapses, relationships, managing emotions and making positive changes in self or lifestyle. Issues related to psychiatric disorders can also be discussed in these groups. Specific problems and issues discussed in groups include, but are not limited to the following:

Motivational struggles such as loss of, or lowered desire to stay substance free, deal with a psychiatric disorder, or make personal and lifestyle changes. Motivational problems often lead to poor adherence with attending treatment sessions, mutual support programs, or following the recovery plan. Poor adherence in turn often contributes to relapse.

Strong desires, obsessions or craving to use substances. These are common in the early months of recovery from SUDs. Failure to pay attention to these can lead to a client becoming overwhelmed and giving in to the strong craving or obsession to use. Clients are taught to share their desires rather than keep them private as this gives them greater control over what they can do to manage these cravings or desires for substances.

Lapses or relapses to alcohol or other drug use. Group members vary widely in their experiences with lapses or relapses. Some have none, others have one, and others have multiple relapses during the course of treatment. The focus is on trying to get the group member to develop a desire to initiate and maintain abstinence by following a recovery plan. If a group member is unable to stabilize from a lapse or relapse, the group leader should consider other types of treatment at a higher level of care (e.g., move from an IOP to s residential; move from outpatient to IOP; go to a detoxification program if physical addiction occurs and the client cannot safely stop using substances or has a history of complications such as seizures related to withdrawing from drugs like alcohol.

Giving up the main substance of use but continuing to use other substances. Although total abstinence is the main goal of treatment, some group members will not accept this and may continue to use substances other than their primary drug of choice. The use of these substances increases the risk of relapse to the primary drug of choice. Opioid- and cocaine- addicted clients often use alcohol or marijuana. Some opioid-addicted clients use and misuse prescription medications, especially pain and anti-anxiety medicines.

Any significant changes in psychiatric symptoms and how these are affecting the group member (and family or significant others). If a client expresses suicidality, the group leader should explore this in group and meet with the client after the session to determine what interventions may be needed to address this and keep the client safe.

Problems in mutual support program participation. Members vary in their use of programs such as AA, NA, CA, CMA, other 12-Step programs or other mutual support programs. While attendance is highly encouraged, some clients refuse to attend, attend only occasionally, or participate minimally. They do not get a sponsor, work the steps or attend social functions sponsored by NA, CA or AA. Some members discuss concrete problems such as conflicts with a sponsor or other members or being offered substances by a member of a mutual support program.

Boredom with recovery and the feeling that life is not much better despite being off of alcohol or drugs. Many individuals like excitement, action and "living on the edge." Recovery can be a major adjustment for them. Recovery often is much less exciting the feelings produced by certain drugs, wheeling and dealing on the streets, getting over on other people and partying. Some members also experience boredom with their relationships, job or other aspects of life, which is a different type of boredom requiring careful consideration before major decisions are made.

Managing emotions such as anger, anxiety, depression or guilt and shame. Inability to use active coping strategies to manage emotions is a major factor in many relapses to alcohol or drug use following a period of recovery. Group members often benefit from learning emotional management skills such as being able to identify and recognize feelings, accept them, and learn to live with them without using substances. In some instances, an emotional state (e.g., anxiety or depression) can be part of a psychiatric disorder that may require treatment.

Relationship problems or conflicts with family members, friends or colleagues at work. Interpersonal problems run the gamut from mildly problematic to severe ones that pose a major threat to recovery or well-being. Specific problems or issues often discussed include conflicts or disputes with others, anger or disappointment at others, emotional or physical violence, or inappropriate sexual interactions (e.g., unprotected sex, sex with a stranger, sexual promiscuity). Involvement in relationships that are non-supportive or characterized by lack of reciprocity, difficulty saying no or setting limits with others, and difficulty asking others for help or support are other problems that may be explored in group sessions.

Relationships within the group. Group members may have strong feelings towards each other that impact on their participation in a therapy group and their recovery. It is not unusual for group members to exhibit problems in interpersonal style in a therapy group, especially one that occurs over a long period of time so that members get to know each other. These dynamics show in numerous ways. A few examples include a group member: criticizing another group member, not responding to a member's emotional pain, showing anger towards a member, avoiding eye contact or direct conversation with a group member,

Psychiatric disorders or other types of SUDs. In some instances, group members will have co-morbid psychiatric disorders or other compulsive disorders (e.g., gambling, sex, internet, spending) that contribute to difficulty with emotional states, interfere with recovery, cause personal distress, or contribute to suicidal feelings. Some members may also have other SUDs or excessive behaviors such as compulsive gambling, sex, spending or work. While the group is not intended as a therapy group for mental health disorders unless part of a co-occurring disorders program, these problems may be discussed in the context of recovery from SUDs. The group leader should encourage members with psychiatric disorders to get an appropriate evaluation to determine if psychiatric treatment is needed in addition to SUDs treatment. The leader can also offer to help facilitate this evaluation if needed.

Other psychosocial problems discussed include those related to: School, work, housing, finances, the legal system, or how to structure leisure time. Engaging in substance-free activities is an issue frequently discussed in these groups.

Problems Encountered in the Group Process

In addition to specific problems related to recovery or the lives of the group members, problems are also commonly encountered in the group process. These problems require the group counselor to intervene to make sure the group addresses them. Following is an analysis of some common group process problems and suggested strategies for the counselor:

A group member dominates the session or always brings it back to his own problems or issues.

The group counselor can thank the member for the contributions and then elicit opinions and experiences from other group members. If the group member persistently tries to dominate group conversations or turns the topic back to his own problems or issues, this behavior pattern can be pointed out by the group counselor to make this member and other group members aware of the behavior. The other members can be asked how they feel about the member's dominating the session, and how they want to deal with this in a way that is satisfying to everyone in the group. Even though this creates a problem on one level, on another level some group members find that it creates a safety net for them because they may believe they do not have to self-disclose personal problems or feelings as long as another member is taking up the group time.

A group member does not disclose any problem or open up in the group session.

The group counselor can share his observations about the member's behavior and generalize the issues by asking group members to talk about any difficulties that contribute to problems in self-disclosing (e.g., shame, shyness, social anxiety). Participants can then focus on ways this member (or other group members who have trouble self-disclosing) can gradually learn to trust the group and disclose personal thoughts, feelings, problems or concerns.

A member rejects the input, advice or feedback of other group members.

The group counselor can point out this pattern and engage the group in a discussion of why this pattern is occurring. Members who offer help and support only to have their attempts rejected can be asked to talk about what this feels like so that the member rejecting their help is aware of the impact of this behavior pattern on others.

A member only pays attention when the topic focuses on his problems or interrupts others when they talk.

The group counselor can point out his observations of the group member and discuss the reasons for this behavior. The group can then engage in an examination of the effects of this behavior (e.g., upsets other members, turns them off, makes them feel like their problems aren't important) and the importance of "giving and receiving" mutual support by listening to each other's concerns and problems.

A member who wants easy answers to problems or is quick to provide easy solutions to others when they discuss personal problems.

The group counselor can share his observations of this behavior and ask the group to discuss the importance of taking responsibility to find solutions to their problems, and to identify more than one strategy to address a particular problem. The leader can emphasize that while there are different alternative ways to resolve specific problems, seldom are there easy or simple solutions, and that time, patience and persistence are needed for group members to resolve problems. When a group member provides an easy solution, the group counselor can acknowledge that this is one strategy that may help some people, but that it is also helpful to have other strategies. The Counselor can then engage the group in an exploration of other strategies to address the problem under discussion. Finally, the group counselor can emphasize to the group that learning how to think about problem solving is just as important as dealing with specific problems since everyone in the group will continue to face multiple problems in their ongoing recovery.

A member tries to use the group counselor for individual therapy during the group session.

The group counselor can ask other group members to comment on the problems or issues presented by this member to engage the group in an open dialogue. Group members can also be asked how they relate to the problem or issue presented on a personal level. If the group member asks the counselor how to handle a specific problem, he can encourage the member to directly ask peers in the group their ideas on dealing with this problem. This helps members learn to use group support.

Members who arrive late for the group session or want to leave during discussions.

The leader and group should decide on a rule regarding lateness to group. Sometimes, there are legitimate reasons for being late (e.g., the bus a member takes was running 15 minutes late, the member got a flat tire, etc.). Members may be given a break once or twice for being late. Or, the group may establish a rule in which the member cannot join the group after a certain amount of time (e.g., more than 5–10 minutes after the start of the group). If time limits are not set, some members will often be late as long as this behavior is tolerated. Members who are persistently late can be asked to discuss this pattern of behavior, how it shows in other areas of life, and what they think needs to be done to change this pattern. Group members should never leave the session unless some emergency occurs. Routinely allowing people to walk in and out disrupts the flow of the conversation and gives the message that what members say is not important because people can leave at any time. Members may want to leave group due to boredom, feeling like the chosen topics do not relate to them, or as a way to avoid personally discussing problems or feelings

The group talks in generalities and avoids exploring specific problems in depth.

The group counselor can point out this dynamic to the group and ask them to discuss why they aren't talking about specific problems or concerns in recovery. Members can then be asked to set the agenda in a concrete way so that specific problems or concerns are identified to be explored in group. It isn't uncommon for group members to view counseling groups no different from free floating discussions held in some NA or AA meetings. However, group therapy sessions are designed to explore and solve problems and not simply be a repetition of 12-Step recovery meetings.

The group avoids confronting a member who behaves inappropriately.

The group counselor can point out this dynamic and ask the group what they think about the inappropriate behavior, and what led to their avoiding confronting it. Members should not be allowed to use or check their phones during the sessions.

Other problems may occur during the group time, but these are some of the ones that we have seen over the past several years conducting groups or reviewing hundreds of tapes of group sessions. We wish to stress again that while the "content" (i.e., problems and issues discussed) of the group is important, if the "process" bogs down, not much will get accomplished. In addition, some group members may miss sessions or drop out as a result of process problems that aren't addressed. Unfortunately, group members may avoid dealing with these issues directly so the group counselor won't always know the reasons for a member's poor attendance or early drop out from group. In our experience, it is not uncommon for members to be upset over process issues. A "preventive" strategy is to periodically engage the group in a discussion of the group process. The group counselor can ask what they think about the group sessions, what they like and dislike about how the group has been going, and what they would like to see different in the group.

CHAPTER 8

Relapse and the Family

IMPACT OF DISORDERS AND RELAPSE ON THE FAMILY

Many types of psychiatric illness are chronic or recurrent conditions in which relapse (sometimes called recurrence) is common, and more severe substance use disorders such as addiction or dependence is also characterized by relapse. In fact, it is not unusual for a person to need multiple episodes of treatment over time before stable recovery is established.

We have met and talked with many families over the years, and conducted several surveys to learn about the experience of families dealing with a loved with a substance use, psychiatric, or co-occurring disorder who has relapsed. Our clinical experiences with individual families and groups of families, results of these surveys, and other clinical and research publications show that families and their members are affected in both positive and negative ways by a loved one's disorders and relapses. The actual impact depends on the type and severity of the disorders, the history of relapse and the severity of any current relapse episode, behaviors, and whether the impaired individual engages in treatment and recovery following a relapse.

Effects on the family and its members are also determined by a family member's ability to manage stress and cope with the problems caused or worsened by their loved one's relapse, as well as access to support from relatives, friends or others in family support programs. If a family member has a confidante and supportive people to rely on, this can counteract some of the negative effects of a member's disorders and relapse. The more a family member learns "self-care," the less negatively they may be affected by a loved one's relapse.

Positive effects of relapse include a family member building resilience and strengths, and being able to offer help and support to others affected by a loved one's relapse. Some families become more cohesive and supportive with each other when dealing with a member's relapse. Family members often learn from each other when they share their experiences and positive coping strategies that have helped them manage their own reactions to relapse.

Any area of family life can be affected in negative ways by a relapse including the family mood or atmosphere, how members communicate or solve (or avoid) problems, interact and spend time together, lifestyle and financial condition, and whether they are exposed to serious problems such as violence, neglect, abuse, or suicidality of the affected member. Some specific examples shared with us by family members include the following:

Emotional burden: Common emotions experienced include anger, bitterness, resentment, hatred; depression, sadness, despair, despondency; anxiety, worry, fear or obsession; guilt, shame, embarrassment; or feeling helpless or hopeless. Some family members report feeling emotionally and physically exhausted from dealing with the chaos associated with a loved one's disorders. Many families have experienced multiple relapses of a loved one, which affects their attitudes, behaviors and emotional states. Some have even been shocked when a highly motivated family member was stable in recovery for a very long time only to have a relapse. Sometimes, this was totally unexpected and shocked the family.

A confusing experience for some families is that negative emotions can be experienced not only during the active phase of the illness or after a relapse, but even when their loved one is in recovery and doing well. These emotions can persist or return at any time. The best way for families to counteract strong emotions is understanding these disorders and learning ways to manage their own reactions and focus on self-care. In addition to learning positive coping strategies in dealing with a relapse and one's personal reactions, some family members may need help for a more serious problem such as clinical depression.

Family break-up: This may be caused by separation, divorce or violence. Or, in some cases, children go to live with other relatives or are in the custody of Children and Youth Services (usually as a result of violence, abuse or neglect by a parent).

Many parents of young adults with an addiction have shared the stresses associated with having to take care of their grandchildren when their adult son or daughter relapsed or ended up in rehab or jail. Despite loving them dearly, some grandparents do not have the time or resources to give these grandchildren what they need. This sometimes creates an additional burden of feeling guilty in addition to trying to make sense of the relapse.

Role reversal: Family members may take over the responsibilities of the member with the disorder. This includes parental responsibilities as mentioned above, as well as financial and other responsibilities.

In some instances when a parent is seriously impaired by their problems, a child may act like a surrogate parent to younger siblings. This child may seem to be doing well in life, but may internalize negative feelings such as sadness, depression or anxiety.

Family rituals and shared activities: The way a family shares time together, engages in family rituals or celebrates (or avoids celebrating) special occasions can be harmed. We are aware of situations in which a relapse has occurred during an important family event (e.g., a wedding or graduation), thus causing bad feelings among family members.

Communication: There may be too much arguing, too much focus on negative feelings and interactions, and expression of negative feelings towards one another. Or, the member who relapsed may be the recipient of angry, negative comments expressed by frustrated and upset family members.

Financial condition and lifestyle: Many families report spending considerable amounts of money on problems caused or worsened by their loved one, costs associated with the legal system, or costs associated with treatment. When underemployment or loss of a job is involved, the family may also experience negative financial consequences such as being unable to pay bills or live comfortably.

Effects on children: Children are at higher risk for a substance use or psychiatric disorder if a parent has one of these disorders. For example, many studies and reports have documented the negative effects of addiction on children such as: increased risk for a substance use or psychiatric disorder (especially depression or anxiety), medical problems, academic problems and problems associated with impulsive behaviors. When a parent relapses after a period of stable recovery, children as well as adults can have a reaction to this.

FAMILY GROUPS

Many treatment programs offer family groups to help members learn about and deal with issues related to substance use and psychiatric disorders, or relapse. Family groups may include: a one-time educational and support group (1 hour to a full day); several educational and support group sessions over time (variable length of time); or ongoing groups that provide support, education, and opportunities to address family problems and teach coping strategies to manage personal reactions to a loved one with a disorder or a relapse.

Goals of group sessions may include providing education or support, helping people feel comfortable talking with their loved one about relapse issues and plans to reduce relapse risk, learning coping strategies, or increasing self-care activities. Many family members get so focused on the impaired member that they do not give enough time and attention to other family members or their own needs, especially when a relapse occurs. The family can learn not to tie in their emotional stability to their impaired member's recovery or relapse.

Involving the family in treatment can help the person with the disorder as well as the family unit and its members. Benefits include:

- Providing treatment staff with input about the impaired family member, and any history of recovery and relapse.

- Helping improve the member's compliance with treatment so they get the maximum benefit from professional care, which can reduce relapse risk.

- The family can share their experiences, feelings and concerns related to dealing with their loved one and the impact they have experienced over time, including relapses.

- The affected family member can learn what it has been like for the family, and their concerns and worries if they believe a relapse is imminent or has actually occurred.

- The family can provide support to their loved one to help their recovery and possibly reduce their risk of relapse.

- The family can gain education about the disorder (symptoms, causes, effects, treatment, recovery) and relapse (warning signs, risk factors, strategies to reduce risk of relapse).

- Family members who present significant emotional distress can be encouraged to get help for themselves (therapy, medication, mutual support programs).

- A family member can learn about mutual support programs for families, and how these may be of help to the family and its members.

- Family members can learn about behaviors that do not help their loved one as well as behaviors that do help this member, both before and after a relapse.

- Members from different families can learn from each other and provide each other with help and support in dealing with their loved ones' relapses.

- Family members can learn positive coping strategies to take care of themselves as well as deal with the effects of a relapse that they have experienced.

MULTIPLE FAMILY GROUPS

Some treatment programs offer education and support groups to multiple families. These are usually structured and cover specific topics. Sessions may last from several hours to several days. Possible content covered, depending on time available, may include:

- Overview of substance use, psychiatric and co-occurring disorders: types and symptoms of the more common disorders and causes of disorders.

- Effects of disorders on the person (medical, emotional, social, spiritual, other); and how each type of disorder can affect the other.

- Treatment options: programs, types of therapies, and medications used to treat various psychiatric or addictive disorders.

- Other resources for the impaired member: community programs or resources that can help with specific problems or needs (housing, vocational, financial, spiritual).

- How the family can help support their loved one.

- The impact of disorders on the family.

- Professional resources available to help the family.

- Mutual support programs for families.

- Relapse: common warning signs, high-risk factors, the need to anticipate and prepare for relapse; and intervening early should a relapse occur.

MUTUAL SUPPORT PROGRAMS FOR FAMILIES

Many families initially get involved in treatment mainly to help their loved one. However, due to the emotional burden and other problems experienced, they may benefit from ongoing participation in a family support group. These include support groups for families with a member who has a psychiatric illness, or an addiction.

Exposure to members active in support groups can help families connect to these programs. Attending and working these programs can help take the focus off of the impaired family member and put it on others who were affected by this member. A result may be that an actual relapse has less of a negative impact on them.

Treatment programs and individual clinicians should examine what they offer, if anything, to family members or significant others related to relapse. A family can be helped by any member of the treatment team to understand and prepare for the possibility of relapse. Many non-family therapy services can help the family including support groups, education groups, and mutual support programs. Families deserve time and attention of professionals to help them increase their ability to cope with the many demands of dealing with a loved one who has a substance use, psychiatric or co-occurring disorder, especially one who has relapsed.

Appendices

APPENDIX 1

References

Abel EL. Fetal alcohol syndrome: the 'American Paradox'. *Alcohol and alcoholism (Oxford, Oxfordshire).* 1998;33(3):195–201.

APA. *Diagnostic and Statistical Manual of Mental Disorders, 5th ed.* Washington DC: American Psychiatric Association; 2013.

Baker AL, Hides L, Lubman DI. Treatment of cannabis use among people with psychotic or depressive disorders: a systematic review. *The Journal of clinical psychiatry.* 2010;71(3):247–254.

Beck A, Wright F, Liese B. *Cognitive Therapy of Substance Abuse.* New York: Guilford Press; 1994.

Beck A. *Cognitive Therapy and the Emotional Disorders.* New York: New American Library; 1976.

Bellack AS, Mueser KT, Gingerich S, Agresta J. *Social Skills Training for Schizophrenia, 2nd Ed.* New York: The Guilford Press; 2004.

Bellack AS. Skills training for people with severe mental illness. *Psychiatric Rehabilitation Journal.* 2004;27(4):375–391.

Bertrand J, Floyd LL, Weber MK. Guidelines for identifying and referring persons with fetal alcohol syndrome. *MMWR. Recommendations and reports: Morbidity and mortality weekly report. Recommendations and reports / Centers for Disease Control.* 2005;54(Rr-11):1–14.

Bowen S, Chawla N., Marlatt G.A. *Mindfulness-Based Relapse Prevention for Addictive Behaviors.* New York: Guilford Press; 2011.

Brent DA. *Suicide risk across the lifespan: Comprehensive asseessment and clinical management.* Pittsburgh PA: University of Pittsburgh Medical Center; 2011.

Burns D. *Ten Days To Self-Esteem.* New York: Quill; 1993.

Carroll KM, Rounsaville BJ, Nich C, Gordon LT, Wirtz PW, Gawin F. One-year follow-up of psychotherapy and pharmacotherapy for cocaine dependence. Delayed emergence of psychotherapy effects. *Archives of General Psychiatry.* 1994;51(12):989–997.

Carroll KM. Relapse prevention as a psychosocial treatment: A review of controlled clinical trials. *Experimental and Clinical Psychopharmacology.* 1996;4:46–54.

Center for Disease Control. Injury prevention and control: Suicide prevention. 2014. http://www.cdc.gov/violenceprevention/suicide/.

Clark HW, Power AK, Le Fauve CE, Lopez EI. Policy and practice implications of epidemiological surveys on co-occurring mental and substance use disorders. *Journal of Substance Abuse Treatment.* 2008;34(1):3–13.

Cloninger CR. Genetics of substance abuse. In: Galanter M, Kleber, H.D., ed. *Textbook of Substance Abuse.* 3rd ed. Washington DC: American Psychiatric Publishing Inc.; 2005:73–80.

CSAT. Substance Abuse Treatment for Persons with Co-occurring Disorders. *Treatment Improvement Protocol (TIP).* Rockville, MD: SAMHSA; 2005.

CSAT. Substance abuse treatment reduces family dysfunction, improves productivity. *Substance Abuse Brief.* Rockville, MD: Center for Substance Abuse, Treatment, SAMHSA; 2000.

Daley DC, Donovan DM. *Using 12-Step Programs in Recovery: For Individuals with Alcohol or Drug SUDs.* Murrysville, PA: Daley Publications; 2009.

Daley DC, Douaihy A. *A Family Guide to Addiction and Recovery: Coping Strategies for Family Members.* Murrysville, PA: Daley Publications; 2014.

Daley DC, Douaihy A. Co-Occurring Disorders. In: Douaihy A, Daley DC, eds. *Substance Use Disorders.* New York: Oxford University Press; 2013:283–310.

Daley DC, Douaihy A. *Group Treatments for Addiction: Counseling Strategies for Recovery and Therapy Groups.* Murrysville, PA: Daley Publications; 2011.

Daley DC, Douaihy A. *Recovery and Relapse Prevention for Co-Occurring Disorders.* Murrysville, PA: Daley Publications; 2010.

Daley DC, Douaihy A. *Recovery from Co-Occurring Disorders: Staying Sober and Managing Your Psychiatric Illness.* Murrysville, PA: Daley Publications; 2014.

Daley DC, Douaihy A. *Relapse Prevention for Psychiatric Illness: Strategies to Maintain Recovery.* Murrysville, PA: Daley Publications; 2013.

Daley DC, Douaihy A. *Sober Relationships and Support Systems in Recovery: For Substance Use or Co-Occurring Disorders.* Murrysville, PA: Daley Publications; 2010.

Daley DC, Marlatt GA. *Overcoming Your Alcohol and Drug Problem: Effective Recovery Strategies. Client Workbook.* 2nd ed. New York: Oxford University Press; 2006.

Daley DC, Marlatt GA. *Overcoming Your Alcohol and Drug Problem: Effective Recovery Strategies. Therapist Guide.* 2nd ed. New York: Oxford University Press; 2006.

Daley DC, Miller J. *Addiction in Your Family: Helping Yourself and Your Loved Ones.* Holmes Beach, FL: Learning Publications; 2001.

Daley DC, Moss H. *Dual Disorders: Counseling Clients with Chemical Dependency and Mental Illness, 3rd ed.* Center City, MN: Hazelden; 2002.

Daley DC, Spear J. *A Family Guide to Coping with Dual Disorders.* 2nd ed. Center City, MN: Hazelden; 2003.

Daley DC, Thase M. *Dual Disorders Recovery Counseling: Integrated Treatment for Substance Use and Mental Health Disorders, 3rd ed.* Independence, MO: Independence Press; 2004.

Daley DC, Zuckoff A. Improving compliance with the initial outpatient session among discharged inpatient dual diagnosis clients. *Social Work.* 1998;43(5):470–473.

Daley DC, Zuckoff A. *Improving Treatment Compliance: Counseling and System Strategies for Substance Use and Dual Disorders.* Center City, MN: Hazelden; 1999.

Daley DC. *Mood Disorders and Addiction: A Guide for Clients, Families and Providers.* New York: Oxford University Press; 2006.

Daley DC. Motivation from the Inside Out: The Client's Perspective. *Counselor.* 2014;15(4):26–28.

Daley DC. *Recovery from Co-Occurring Disorders: Strategies for Managing SUDs and Mental Health Disorders.* 4th ed. Independence, MO: Independence Press; 2011.

Daley DC. *Relapse Prevention Workbook for Recovering Alcoholics and Drug Dependent Persons.* 5th ed. Murrysville, PA: Daley Publications; 2013.

Daley DC. *Relapse. Conceptual, Research and Clinical Perspectives.* New York: Haworth; 1988.

Daley DC. *Sobriety Journal.* Murrysville, PA: Daley Publications; 2005.

Daley DC. *Think Sober, Live Sober: Strategies to Overcome Negative Thinking.* Murrysville, PA: Daley Publications; 2013.

Daley DC. Understanding and addressing suicide. *Counselor Connection.* October, 2014, pp 1-4.

Deykin EY, Buka SL. Prevalence and risk factors for posttraumatic stress disorder among chemically dependent adolescents. *The American Journal of Psychiatry.* 1997;154(6):752–757.

Diener E, Biswas-Diener R. *Happiness: Unlocking the Mysteries of Psychological Wealth.* Malden, MA: Blackwell Publishing; 2008.

Donovan DM, Daley DC, Brigham GS, et al. Stimulant abuser groups to engage in 12-step: a multisite trial in the National Institute on Drug Abuse Clinical Trials Network. *Journal of substance abuse treatment.* 2013;44(1):103–114.

Donovan DM. Assessment of Addictive Behaviors for Relapse Prevention. In: Donovan DM, Marlatt GA, eds. *Assessment of Addictive Behaviors, 2nd Ed.* New York: The Guilford Press; 2005.

Douaihy A. Hepatitis C Virus, Human Immunodeficiency Virus, And Substance Use Disorders. In: Douaihy A, Daley DC, eds. *Substance Use Disorders.* New York: Oxford University Press; 2013.

Emmons RA. *Thanks! How the New Science of Gratitude Can Make You Happier.* NY: Houghton Mifflin Company; 2007.

Enright RD. *The Forgiving Life: A Pathway to Overcoming Resentment and Creating a Legacy of Love.* Washington DC: American Psychological Association; 2012.

Flynn PM, Brown BS. Co-occurring disorders in substance abuse treatment: issues and prospects. *Journal of Substance Abuse Treatment.* 2008;34(1):36–47.

Fredrickson B. *Positivity: Top-Notch Research Reveals the 3 to 1 Ratio That Will Change Your Life.* NY: Three Rivers Press; 2009.

Funk RR, McDermeit M, Godley SH, Adams L. Maltreatment issues by level of adolescent substance abuse treatment: the extent of the problem at intake and relationship to early outcomes. *Child Maltreatment.* 2003;8(1):36–45.

Galanter M, Kleber HD. *Textbook of Substance Abuse Treatment.* 4th ed. Washington DC: American Psychiatric Publishing, Inc.; 2008.

Garbutt JC, West SL, Carey TS, Lohr KN, Crews FT. Pharmacological treatment of alcohol dependence: a review of the evidence. *JAMA* 1999;281(14):1318–1325.

Gingerich S, Mueser KT. *Illness Management and Recovery: Personalized Skills and Strategies for Those with Mental Illness, 3rd Ed.* Center City, MN: Hazelden; 2011.

Gorelick DA. Pharmacologic Interventions for Cocaine, Methamphetamine, and Other Stimulant Addiction. In: Ries RK, Fiellin DA, Miller SC, Saitz R, eds. *The ASAM Principles of Addiction Medicine, 5th Ed.* Philadelphia PA: Wolters Kluwer Health; 2014.

Gorski TT, Miller M. *Counseling for Relapse Prevention.* Independence, MO: Herald House/ Independence Press; 1982.

Greater Good Science Center. 2001; www.greatergood.berkeley.edu.

HIV infection among injection-drug users - 34 states, 2004–2007. *MMWR. Morbidity and Mortality Weekly Report.* 2009;58(46):1291–1295.

Horsfall J, Cleary M, Hunt GE, Walter G. Psychosocial treatments for people with co-occurring severe mental illnesses and substance use disorders (dual diagnosis): a review of empirical evidence. *Harvard Review of Psychiatry.* 2009;17(1):24–34.

Irvin JE, Bowers CA, Dunn ME, Wang MC. Efficacy of relapse prevention: a meta-analytic review. *Journal of Consulting and Clinical Psychology.* 1999;67(4):563–570.

Kadden R, Carbonari J, Litt M, Tonigan S, Zweben A. Matching Alcoholism Treatments to Client Heterogeneity: Project MATCH Three-Year Drinking Outcomes. *Alcoholism: Clinical and Experimental Research.* 1998;22(6):1300–1311.

Kelly TM, Daley D, Douaihy A. Contingency management for patients with dual disorders in intensive Outpatient treatment for addiction. *Journal of Dual Diagnosis.* 2014;10(3):108–117.

Kelly TM, Daley DC, Douaihy AB. Treatment of substance abusing patients with comorbid psychiatric disorders. *Addictive Behaviors.* 2012;37(1):11–24.

Keltner D, Marsh J, Smith JA, eds. *The Compassionate Instinct: The Science of Human Goodness.* NY: W.W. Norton and Company; 2010.

Kingston S, Raghavan C. The relationship of sexual abuse, early initiation of substance use, and adolescent trauma to PTSD. *Journal of Traumatic Stress.* 2009;22(1):65–68.

Kmiec J, Cornelius J, Douaihy A. Pharmacotheraphy of Substance Use Disorders. In: Douaihy A, Daley DC, eds. *Substance Use Disorders.* New York: Oxford University Press; 2013:169–212.

Kranzler HR, Burleson JA, Del Boca FK, et al. Buspirone treatment of anxious alcoholics. A placebo-controlled trial. *Archives of General Psychiatry.* 1994;51(9):720–731.

Kresina TF, Hoffman K, Lubran R, Clark HW. Integrating hepatitis services into substance abuse treatment programs: new initiatives from SAMHSA. *Public health reports (Washington, D.C.: 1974).* 2007;122 Suppl 2:96–98.

Kurtz MM, Mueser KT. A meta-analysis of controlled research on social skills training for schizophrenia. *Journal of Consulting and Clinical psychology.* 2008;76(3):491–504.

Liberman R. *Social and Independent Living Skills: Symptoms Mangement Module. Patient Workbook.* Los Angeles, CA: Author; 1987.

Linehan M. *Cognitive Behavioral Treatment of Borderline Personality Disorders.* New York: Guilford Press; 1993.

Ling W, Jacobs P, Hillhouse M, et al. From research to the real world: buprenorphine in the decade of the Clinical Trials Network. *Journal of Substance Abuse Treatment.* 2010;38 Suppl 1:S53–60.

Lowinson JH, Ruiz P, Millman RB, Langrod J. *Substance Abuse: A Comprehensive Textbook.* 5th ed. Philadelphia, PA: Lippincott, Williams & Wilkins; 2011.

Luskin F. *Forgive for Love: The Missing Ingredient for a Healthy and Lasting Relationship.* NY: Harper Collins; 2007.

Lyubomirsky S. *The How of Happiness: A Scientific Approach to Getting the Life You Want.* NY: The Penguin Press; 2008.

Maisto SA, McKay JR, O'Farrell TJ. Relapse precipitants and behavioral marital therapy. *Addictive Behaviors.* 1995;20(3):383–393.

Marlatt GA, Donovan DM. *Relapse Prevention: A Self-Control Strategy for the Maintenance of Behavior Change.* 2nd ed. New York: Guilford Press; 2005.

Marlatt GA, Gordon J. *Relapse Prevention: A Self-Control Strategy for the Maintenance of Behavior Change.* New York: Guilford Press; 1985.

Marlatt GA. Cognitive Factors in the Relapse Process. In: Marlatt GA, Gordon J, eds. *Relapse Prevention: A Self-Control Strategy for the Maintenance of Behavior Change.* New York: Guilford Press; 1985a:128–200.

Marlatt GA. Situational determinants of relapse and skill-training interventions. In: Marlatt GA, Gordon J, eds. *Relapse Prevention: A Self-Control Strategy for the Maintenance of Behavior Change.* 2nd ed. New York: Guilford Press; 1985b:71–127.

Marlatt GA. Taxonomy of high-risk situations for alcohol relapse: evolution and development of a cognitive-behavioral model. *Addiction (Abingdon, England).* 1996;91 Suppl:S37–49.

Mattson SN, Roesch SC, Glass L, et al. Further development of a neurobehavioral profile of fetal alcohol spectrum disorders. *Alcoholism, Clinical and Experimental Research.* 2013;37(3):517–528.

McCrady BS. Relapse Prevention: A Couple's Therapy Perspective. In: O'Farrell TJ, ed. *Treating Alcohol Problems: Marital and Family Interventions.* New York: Guilford Press; 1989:165–182.

McFarlane WR. *Multifamily Groups in the Traetment of Severe Psychiatric Disorders.* New York: The Guilford Press; 2002.

McKay JR. Studies of factors in relapse to alcohol, drug and nicotine use: a critical review of methodologies and findings. *Journal of Studies on Alcohol.* 1999;60(4):566–576.

McLellan AT, Lewis DC, O'Brien CP, Kleber HD. Drug dependence, a chronic medical illness: implications for treatment, insurance, and outcomes evaluation. *JAMA.* 2000;284(13):1689–1695.

McMain S, Sayrs JHR, Dimeff LA, Linehan MM. Dialectical Behavior Therapy for Individuals with Borderline Personality Disorder and Substance Dependence. In: Dimeff LA, Koerner K, eds. *Dialectical Behavior Therapy in Clinical Practice: Applications Across Disorders and Settings.* New York: The Guilford Press; 2007:145–173.

Miller WR, Rollnick S. *Motivational Interviewing: Preparing People for Change.* 3rd ed. New York: Guilford Press; 2012.

Monti P, Adams D, Kadden RM, al. e. *Treating Alcohol Dependence.* 2nd ed. New York: Guilford; 2002.

Moss HM, Vanyukow M, Majumder P, al. e. Prepubertal sons of substance abusers: Influences of paternal and familial substance abuse on behavioral disposition, IQ, and school achievement. *Addictive Behaviors.* 1995;20:1–14.

Mueser KT, Drake RE, Miles K. The course and treatment of substance use disorders in persons with severe mental illness. In: Onken L, Blaine J, Genser S, Horton A, eds. *Treatment of Drug-Dependent Individuals with Comorbid Mental Disorders.* Rockville, MD: U.S. Department of Health and Human Services, NIDA Research Monograph 172; 1997:86–109.

Mueser KT, Drake RE. Comorbidity: What have we learned and where are we going? *Clinical Psychology: Science and Practice.* 2007;14(1):64–69.

Mueser KT, Gingerich S. *The Complete Family Guide to Schizophrenia.* New York: The Guilford Press; 2006.

Mueser KT, Gingerich S. Treatment of Co-Occurring Psychotic and Substance Use Disorders. In: Feit MD, Battle SF, eds. *Social Work in Public Health.* Vol 28. Philadelphia PA: Routledge Taylor & Francis Group; 2013:424–439.

Mueser KT, Glynn SM, Cather C, et al. A randomized controlled trial of family intervention for co-occurring substance use and severe psychiatric disorders. *Schizophrenia Bulletin.* 2013;39(3):658–672.

Mueser KT, Glynn SM. *Behavioral Family Therapy for Psychiatric Disorders, 2nd Ed.* Oakland CA: New Harbinger Publications Inc; 1999.

Mueser KT, Noordsky DL, Drake RE, Fox L. *Integrated Treatment for Dual Disorders: A Guide to Effective Practice.* NY: Guilford Press; 2003.

Najavits LM. *Seeking Safety: A Treatment Manual for PTSD and Substance Abuse.* New York: Guilford Publications; 2001.

Neff K. *Self-Compassion.* NY: William Morrow; 2011.

NIAAA. *Combined Behavioral Intervention Manual.* Bethesda, MD: DHHS; 2004.

NIAAA. *Motivational Enhancement Therapy Manual.* Rockville, MD: DHHS; 1995.

NIAAA. *Twelve-Step Facilitation Therapy Manual.* Rockville, MD: DHHS; 1995.

NIDA. *A Cognitive Behavioral Approach: Treating Cocaine SUDs. Therapy Manuals for Drug SUDs, Manual 1.* Rockville, MD: DHHS; 1998.

NIDA. A Decade of Research by the National Drug Abuse Treatment Clinical Trials Network. *Journal of Substance Abuse Treatment.* 2010;38(4):Supplement 1.

NIDA. *A Group Drug Counseling Approach to Treat Cocaine SUDs. Therapy Manuals for Drug SUDs, Manual 4.* Rockville, MD: DHHS; 2002.

NIDA. *An Individual Drug Counseling Approach to Treat Cocaine SUDs. Therapy Manuals for Drug SUDs, Manual 3.* Rockville, MD: DHHS; 1999.

NIDA. *Brief Strategic Family Therapy for Adolescent Drug Abuse. Therapy Manuals for Drug SUDs, Manual 5.* Rockville, MD: DHHS; 2003.

NIDA. *Principles of Drug Addiction Treatment: A Research-Based Guide.* 3rd ed. Bethesda, MD: DHHS; 2013.

NIDA. *Recovery Training and Self-Help.* 2nd ed. Rockville, MD: DHHS; 1994.

NIDA. *The Science of Treatment: Dissemination of Research-Based Drug SUDs Treatment Findings.* Rockville, MD: DHHS; 2008.

NIMH. Mental Health Medications. Vol NIH Publication 12–3929. Rockville, MD: National Institute of Mental Health; 2010.

Nowinski J, Baker S. *The Twelve-Step Facilitation Handbook: A Systematic Approach to Early Recovery from Alcoholism and SUDs.* MN: Hazelden; 2003.

Nunes EV, Weissman MM, Goldstein R, et al. Psychiatric disorders and impairment in the children of opiate addicts: prevalances and distribution by ethnicity. *The American Journal on Addictions / American Academy of Psychiatrists in Alcoholism and Addictions.* 2000;9(3):232–241.

O'Farrell TJ, Choquette KA, Cutter HS. Couples relapse prevention sessions after behavioral marital therapy for male alcoholics: outcomes during the three years after starting treatment. *Journal of Studies on Alcohol.* 1998;59(4):357–370.

O'Farrell TJ, Fals-Stewart W. *Behavioral Couples Therapy for Alcoholism and Drug Abuse.* New York: Guilford Press; 2006.

O'Farrell TJ, Fals-Stewart W. Continuing Recovery: Maintenance and Relapse Prevention. *Behavioral Couples Therapy for Alcoholism and Drug Abuse.* New York: Guilford Press; 2006:161–187.

O'Farrell TJ. Couples Relapse Prevention Sessions After a Behavioral Marital Therapy Couples Group Program. In: O'Farrell TJ, ed. *Treating Alcohol Problems: Marital and Family Interventions.* New York: Guilford Press; 1993:305–326.

O'Malley SS, Jaffe AJ, Chang G, Schottenfeld RS, Meyer RE, Rounsaville B. Naltrexone and coping skills therapy for alcohol dependence. A controlled study. *Archives of General Psychiatry.* 1992;49(11):881–887.

Poordad F, Hezode C, Trinh R, et al. ABT-450/r-ombitasvir and dasabuvir with ribavirin for hepatitis C with cirrhosis. *The New England Journal of Medicine.* 2014;370(21):1973–1982.

Ralph RO, Corrigan PW, eds. *Recovery in Mental Illness: Broadening Our Understanding of Wellness.* Washington DC: American Psychological Association; 2005.

Rawson RA, Marinelli-Casey P, Anglin MD, et al. A multi-site comparison of psychosocial approaches for the treatment of methamphetamine dependence. *Addiction (Abingdon, England).* 2004;99(6):708–717.

Rawson RA, Obert JL, McCann MJ, Ling W. *The MATRIX Model: Intensive Outpatient Alcohol and Drug Treatment. Therapist Manual.* Center City, MN: Hazelden; 2005.

Recommendations for prevention and control of hepatitis C virus (HCV) infection and HCV-related chronic disease. Centers for Disease Control and Prevention. *MMWR. Recommendations and reports: Morbidity and mortality weekly report. Recommendations and reports / Centers for Disease Control.* 1998;47(Rr-19):1–39.

Regier DA, Farmer ME, Rae DS, et al. Comorbidity of mental disorders with alcohol and other drug abuse. Results from the Epidemiologic Catchment Area (ECA) Study. *JAMA.*   1990;264(19):2511–2518.

Ries RK, Fiellin DA, Miller SC, Saitz R. *Principles of Addiction Medicine.* 5th ed. New York: Lippiincott, Williams, & Wilkins; 2014.

Roberts T. *The Mindfulness Workbook: A Beginner's Guide to Overcoming Fear and Embracing Compassion.* Oakland, CA: New Harbinger Publications; 2009.

Sacks S, Sacks J, De Leon G, Bernhardt AI, Staines GL. Modified therapeutic community for mentally ill chemical "abusers": background; influences; program description; preliminary findings. *Substance Use & Misuse.* 1997;32(9):1217–1259.

SAMHSA. *Addressing suicidal thoughts and behaviors in substance abuse treatment: A treatment improvement protocol TIP 50.* Rockville, MD: Substance Abuse and Mental Health Services Administration;2009.

SAMHSA. Relapse Prevention Therapy. *NREPP: SAMHSA's National Registry of Evidence Based Programs and Practices.* 2008. http://www.nrepp.samhsa.gov/.

SAMHSA's Working Definition of Recovery, 10 Guiding Principles of Recovery. 2012; http://store.samhsa.gov/product/SAMHSA-s-Working-Definition-of-Recovery/PEP12-RECDEF.

Saunders B, Allsop S. Alcohol problems and relapse: Can the clinic combat the community? *Journal of Community Applied Social Psychology.* 1991;1(3):213–221.

Seligman M. *Flourish.* NY: Pocket Books (Simon & Schuster); 2010.

Smalley SL, Winston D. *Fully Present: The Science, Art and Practice of mindfulness.* Philadelphia, PA: Da Capo Press; 2010.

Smelson DA, Dixon L, Craig T, et al. Pharmacological treatment of schizophrenia and co-occurring substance use disorders. *CNS drugs.* 2008;22(11):903–916.

Swanson AJ, Pantalon MV, Cohen KR. Motivational interviewing and treatment adherence among psychiatric and dually diagnosed patients. *The Journal of Nervous and Mental Disease.* 1999;187(10):630–635.

Tartar R, Blackson T, Brigham J, Moss H, Caprara G. The Association Between Childhood Irritability and Liability to Substance Use in Early Adolescence: A Two-Year Follow-Up Study of Boys at Risk for Substance Abuse. *Drug and Alcohol Dependence.* 1995;39:253–261.

van Zaane J, van den Brink W, Draisma S, Smit JH, Nolen WA. The effect of moderate and excessive alcohol use on the course and outcome of patients with bipolar disorders: a prospective cohort study. *The Journal of clinical psychiatry.* 2010;71(7):885–893.

Volkow NHD, Fowler JS. SUD's A Disease of Compulsion and Drive: Involvement of the Orbitofrontal Cortex. *Cerebral Cortex.* 2000;10:318–325.

Weiss RD, Connery HS. *Integrated Group Therapy for Bipolar Disorder and Substance Abuse.* New York: Guilford Press; 2011.

White WL, Kurtz E, Sanders M. *Recovery Management.* Chicago, IL: Great Lakes SUDs Technology Center, University of Illinois at Chicago; 2006.

WHO. Health topics: Suicide. 2014. http://www.who.int/topics/suicide/en.

Worthington EL. *A Just Forgiveness: Responsible Healing Without Excusing Injustice.* Downers Grove, IL: InterVarsity Press; 2012.

Wykes T, Steel C, Everitt B, Tarrier N. Cognitive behavior therapy for schizophrenia: effect sizes, clinical models, and methodological rigor. *Schizophrenia Bulletin.* 2008;34(3):523–537.

APPENDIX 2

Websites

Al-Anon Family Groups	www.alanon.alateen.org
Alcoholics Anonymous	www.alcoholics-anonymous.org
American Psychological Association	www.apa.org
American Psychiatric Association	www.psych.org
Dennis C. Daley	www.drdenniscdaley.com
Dual Recovery Anonymous (DRA)	www.draonline.org
Guilford Publications, Inc.	www.guilford.com
Hazelden Educational Materials	www.hazelden.org
Herald House, Independence Press	www.heraldhouse.org/
Nar-Anon Family Groups	www.naranon.org
Narcotics Anonymous	www.na.org
National Alliance for the Mentally Ill	www.nami.org
National Clearinghouse for Alcohol & Drug Information	www.higherdcenter.org/resources/national-clearinghouse-alcohol-and-drug-information-ncadi
National Institute of Mental Health	www.nimh.nih.gov
National Institute on Alcohol Abuse and Alcoholism	www.niaaa.nih.gov
National Institute on Drug Abuse	www.nida.nih.gov
National Mental Health Association	www.nmha.org
PESI	www.pesi.com
Substance Abuse and Mental Health Services	www.samhsa.gov
U.S. Journal & Health Communications	www.hci-online.com

AMERICAN PSYCHOLOGICAL ASSOCIATION: WWW.APA.ORG

The APA publishes many clinical and empirically-based books for clinicians, which cover a range of psychological disorders. Books are also available on topics such as spirituality, forgiveness and healing as well as treatment of a range of substance use, psychiatric and co-occurring disorders. APA, 750 First Street S.E., Washington, D.C., 20002.

AMERICAN PSYCHIATRIC ASSOCIATION: WWW.PSYCH.ORG

The American Psychiatric Association publishes the *Diagnostic and Statistical Manual of Mental Disorders (DSM IV TR)*, practice guidelines, a book on outcome measures, and many books with the most recent evidenced-based practices for psychiatric and substance use disorders. APA, 1400 K. Street N.W., Washington, D.C., 20005.

DENNIS C. DALEY: WWW.DRDENNISCDALEY.COM

This webpage of the author of this book includes descriptions of materials written for clinicians, clients and families on many topics related to substance use disorders, psychiatric illness, and co-occurring disorders. Dr. Daley was one of the first in the U.S. to write brief, interactive workbooks for recovery from SUDs, and the first to write workbooks for recovery from co-occurring disorders. He and his colleagues wrote the first book for counselors on working with clients with substance use disorders and psychiatric illness. Several of his writings have been translated to foreign languages. Daley Publications, PO Box 161, Murrysville, PA 15668, (724) 727–3640.

NATIONAL INSTITUTE ON ALCOHOL ABUSE AND ALCOHOLISM (NIAAA): WWW.NIH.NIAAA.GOV.

NIAAA has many excellent resources for medical and health professionals, researchers, clients, families and anyone interested in alcohol problems. Some examples of publications for professionals include: Alcohol Alert; Alcohol Research and Health; The 10th Annual Report to Congress on Alcohol and Health; Helping Patients Who Drink Too Much: A Clinician's Guide; many treatment manuals (e.g., manuals for clinicians from project MATCH and COMBINE); a "Graphics Gallery" with pictures used in NIAAA presentations (e.g., pictures of different systems of the body; and pictures related to Fetal Alcohol Syndrome).

Some examples of publications for people with alcohol problems, families or others interested in alcohol problems include: "Drinking and Your Pregnancy; Tips For Cutting Down on Your Drinking; A Family History of Alcoholism: Are You At Risk? and Frequently Asked Questions" (alcohol problems).

NATIONAL INSTITUTE ON DRUG ABUSE (NIDA): WWW.NIH.NIDA.GOV.

NIDA has many resources, including an extensive portfolio of publications, for medical and health professionals, researchers, clients, families, students and young adults, parents and teachers, and anyone interested in alcohol problems. Some examples include facts and information handouts for all drugs of abuse, treatment manuals for clinicians, brief updates on research, clinical resources on evidenced-based treatments (see "Science of SUDs"), an extensive list of publications (including some materials en Espanol) and news articles.

NIDA offers free subscriptions by mail or e-copy to "SUDs Science & Clinical Practice", a peer-reviewed journal for drug abuse researchers and treatment providers, and "NIDA Notes," a brief, 16-page summary of current research sponsored by NIDA.

This webpage has a link to resources on treatment and prevention for medical and health professionals "NIDAMED." This provides extensive information to caregivers and information that can be used with patients who have drug abuse. NIDAMED also includes a drug use screening tool (NM ASSIST), information for referrals for treatment and a link to NIDA's Clinical Trials Network (CTN). The CTN is a national network of medical centers and community treatment programs where research is conducted across a variety of settings with diverse clinical populations. The CTN link provides information on all participants in the CTN and a list of all the specific studies funded. Finally, NIDAMED provides links to other websites of interest to professionals. For example, the "MEDLINEplus Health Information on Substance Abuse" from the National Library of Medicine at NIH provides access to information to professionals and patients on a range of topics related to substance use, substance use disorders and co-occurring disorders.

SUBSTANCE ABUSE & MENTAL HEALTH SERVICES ADMINISTRATION (SAMHSA): WWW.SAMHSA.GOV

SAMHSA has many publications on prevention and treatment of substance use, psychiatric and co-occurring disorders. Similar to the NIAAA and NIDA webpages, this website provides extensive information for medical and health care professionals, researchers, clients, families and anyone interested in substance use and mental health issues. Examples include sections for "Military Families," "Recovery Supports" that promote health and resilience, and a "Data, Outcomes & Quality" section that provides information about the "National Survey on Drug Abuse and Health."

A "**Find Help**" section on the right side of the SAMHSA home page provides information for help on suicide prevention (1–800–273–8255) and a link for "Treatment Locators" so you can find locations for services for substance abuse or mental health problems. A 24-hour helpline is available to aid in locating help with any of these problems (1–800–662–4357).

This webpage provides access to numerous resources for clinicians including the NREPP (National Registry of Evidenced Based Programs and Practices. In addition, 1)

CSAT's Treatment Improvement Protocol (TIP) Series of manuals on numerous specific topics related to SUDs or co-occurring disorders (e.g., adolescent treatment, older adult treatment, detoxification, group therapy, family treatment, medication treatments, etc); these are consensus-based guidelines developed by clinical, research and administrative experts in the field. 2) CSAT's Knowledge Application Program (KAP) gives knowledge about best treatment practices wings by putting it in the hands of providers who help individuals seeking substance abuse treatment. 3) Quick Guides for Clinicians based on the TIP Series. 4) Quick Guides for Administrators based on the TIP Series.

Made in the USA
Monee, IL
27 April 2021